PICTURE POSTCARD VALUES 2009

formerly **IPM** Catalogue of Picture Postcards and Year Book

Compiled by Phil & Dave Smith

Published by:

IPM Promotions
130 Brent Street
Hendon London,
NW4 2DR

Tel: **020 8203 1500**
enqs@ppv.uk.com
www.ppv.uk.com

Repro and Production by:

DX IMAGING
Unit 20,
25 Greenhill Crescent,
Watford, Herts.
WD18 8EA

Tel: 01923 227644
dximaging@dximaging.co.uk

Visit our website at:
www.memoriespostcards.co.uk

FOREWORD

Welcome to the 2009 edition of Picture Postcard Values. This is the 35th edition of the catalogue, which was previously published annually by John Smith as the IPM catalogue.

We welcome new readers and seasoned buyers of the catalogue. All the sections have been reviewed and we have changed prices where necessary. Obviously prices in an annual review such as this do not alter drastically in most cases. We have as usual, improved and added value to this years catalogue of Picture Postcards. The sections which have had major attention and changes are Artists, Aviation, Military, politics, Jewish Postcards, Royalty, Shipping, Theatrical, Sport. This past year has been another good year for the hobby with the Internet providing a great deal of the interest, with some surprisingly high prices. The regular auction houses are also reporting good sales, especially at the higher end, scarcer types in top condition. The more common types are selling well when priced accordingly. Cards which are less scarce are selling well at antique fairs and markets which are outside the mainstream of serious postcard collecting. The fairs are still strong, although there are less of the older dealers and few, if any, new dealers joining the

A new young postie gets ready to deliver postcards for our collections

circuit. However strong the Internet gets I still do not think you can replace the touch and feel of the card to convince you to buy. One of our hobbies greatest attributes is that there are Postcards out there for everyone's taste, every subject is covered, some are easier to find than others. But that is the true pleasure of collecting, the thrill of the search. We have a record number of postcards illustrated this time, which we hope will help your understanding of the pricing. We couldn't have achieved all of this without a great deal of help from our friends. So big thanks to Tony McKendrick, Tom Stanley, Dov Spier, Tony Davis, Chris Newall, Jack Stasiak, for all the expert advice plus the access to your extensive collections.

Good luck and we hope you have a successful year ahead.
Phil and Dave Smith, August 2008

Postcards were the original version of e-mail with several deliveries per day

AN INTRODUCTION TO POSTCARD COLLECTING

Here is a brief introduction to Postcard Collecting, a fascinating and rewarding hobby. We look at the historical background, and view the present state of the art.

The Early Beginnings

The first plain postcards appeared in Austria in 1869. One year later Britain followed, and shortly afterwards in the mid-1870s, the first picture postcards began to appear. The Paris Exhibition of 1889 gave a tremendous boost to this still novel form of sending a message, and from then on picture postcards were produced in ever increasing numbers by almost every country in the world. Britain joined the game in earnest in 1894 when the first picture cards were permitted and in 1902 was the first country to divide the back, thus allowing the message and address on one side and a complete picture on the other, a move which saw an explosion in picture postcard production as other countries quickly followed. This period is dealt with in more detail in the Catalogue under 'Early Cards'.

The Golden Age

The period from 1902-1914 has been termed the 'Golden Age' of picture postcards, for it was in these years that the hobby reached a height of popularity that it has never exceeded. It was a time when nearly everybody sent postcards, because in a pre-telephone era they represented the cheapest and most reliable form of communication. And what cards they were ! Almost every conceivable subject could be found on picture postcards, as publishers competed with each other to produce the most attractive designs. As a result, postcard collecting became a national pastime where almost everybody young or old had their own albums into which went cards showing Father Christmas and Fire Engines, cards showing Pigs, Pretty Ladies and Political Figures, and cards of just about any other subject you care to name! And the hobby was not confined to Britain, for by now every country in the world was producing postcards, resulting in uncountable millions being issued world-wide throughout this period.

World War I

For reasons of quality and price, the majority of British postcards had been printed in Germany, and the guns of 1914 brought this quickly to an end. But although the Great War did see many Patriotic and Military cards issued, in the words of Brian Lund, Editor of Picture Postcard Monthly, It 'destroyed a national mood '.

Between the Wars

From 1918 a number of things combined to bring about a virtual end to the hobby. A nation trying to come to terms with the tragedies of the Somme and of Flanders, was in no mood for the fripperies of the picture postcard. In addition, the doubling of the inland postage rate for postcards, the wider acceptance of the phone as a means of communication, not to mention the difficulties which many firms found themselves in after the war - all these factors combined to bring about the end. Perhaps quite simply, nobody, neither the postcard houses, nor the collectors, wanted to 'start again'. Of course, postcards were still being produced, but in much smaller quantities. The seaside comic market was still there, and some firms were producing local views, while others reflected the current Art Deco craze with some fine issues, but effectively the 'Golden Age' had passed.

World War II

The Second World War saw a minor revival in postcard production, with a number of Military and Aviation series being produced, as well as other cards dealing with issues of the time, but the hobby lay relatively dormant until the late 1950s.

The Postcard Revival

Throughout the post war years, a small band of enthusiasts had kept things going, until in 1959 two collectors, James Butland and Edward Westwood established a regular magazine. 'The Postcard Collectors' Guide & News, full of articles about the hobby, and closing with a short sales list. 1961 saw the foundation by Drene Brennan of the 'Postcard Club of Great Britain', and at this time in the early 1960s, several collectors' shops could be found stocking old postcards. The hobby gathered momentum until in 1968 the compiler of this catalogue established the monthly 'IPM' sales magazine. This was the first real attempt to establish publications for postcards and to put the hobby on to a commercial basis, and this issue also carried the first auction of picture postcards. From then on things further progressed. Postcard Fairs were already being held under the aegis of the PCGB and these were complemented by the first big specialist events held by John Carter, and in the early 1970s by RF Postcards. The hobby received a massive boost with the Victoria & Albert Museum Centenary Exhibition of 1970, later to travel round the country, and supported by an ever increasing number of books, magazines and sales lists, culminated in 1975 with the appearance of the first IPM Catalogue. The following year, 1976, saw the formation of the Postcard Traders Association, the first sale held by "Specialised Postal Auctions', now our leading auction house, and the foundation of the annual British International Postcard Exhibition, while in 1977 came the first Postcard Fair at Bloomsbury Crest Hotel, now an institution among collectors. Our regular monthly journal 'Picture Postcard Monthly' first saw the light of day in 1978, and set the seal on what has become known as the postcard revival. For now we had the dealers, the collectors, the fairs and auctions, and the magazines, books and literature. Everything was there, ready to move postcard collecting into the national hobby it has now become, taking its place alongside Stamps and Coins as one of the top three collecting hobbies in the country.

The Present Day

The hobby today supports some 500 Dealers and many more smaller collector/dealers. The internet has changed postcard collecting, with thousands of Postcards available, all categorised and easy to find with the search engines available. There are an estimated 20,000 serious collectors, many of whom belong to one of nearly 70 Postcard Clubs. We have over 20 Auction Houses specialising in picture postcards, and a national network of Postcard Fairs. There is the PPV Postcard Catalogue, a national magazine, and a substantial number of books on the subject. We can now look briefly at the operation of the hobby today.

The Collectors

Why do people collect picture postcards? Why do people collect anything! For pleasure, interest, and perhaps profit, are some of the reasons which may be advanced. Yet in this hobby, the collecting of postcards is now divided into two worlds. That of Art & Subject Cards, and that of Topographical, or Local History. The former are perhaps the 'real' postcard collectors, while the latter group are essentially more interested in representations of their own locality as it used to be, than in picture postcards as an art form.

The Dealers

The Postcard Trade operates in much the same way as the Stamp or Coin Trade, in that we have a national network of dealers whose task it is to find and supply postcards to collectors. Many of them carry substantial stocks of up to 100,000 cards, all priced, and filed in boxes or albums under their respective Subject or Location headings, although others carry smaller stocks, perhaps specialising in several chosen themes or areas. Many dealers will conduct business through the post, sending approval selections of your choice, while many more can be found at Postcard Fairs throughout the country. A comprehensive list of dealers will be found in 'Picture Postcard Annual', while dates of current Fairs are listed in 'Picture Postcard Monthly.

Auctions

There are now 20 Auction Houses holding regular specialised sales of picture postcards. All produce catalogues obtainable on subscription, and all will accept postal bids for the Lots on offer. While the more common cards tend to be lotted in some quantity, there is now an increasing trend for the better cards to be offered as individual items in single lots, a reflection of the current strong demand for these cards. A word of advice, when buying at auction do try to ensure that cards are in the best possible condition, particularly if buying through a postal bid. This is made easy by certain leading Auction firms, whose descriptions always include a very clear statement of condition, but is less visible in the catalogues of some firms, where at times you will find nothing at all regarding condition.

Fairs
Led by the gigantic IPM Promotions Fair which has been held every month for 30 years at Bloomsbury, London WC1, there are now over 50 organisations holding regular Postcard Fairs throughout the country, dates of which may be checked with the Diary published in 'Picture Postcard Monthly'. The largest monthly fair is the 'Bloomsbury', which every month has up to 90 stands packed with picture postcards and related ephemera, Other large provincial events include the 2-day Fairs held at York, Twickenham, Woking and Shepton Mallet, with major one day events at Cheltenham, Birmingham, Nottingham, Wickham and Haywards Heath. The prestige event, and most important show of the year, is the annual Picture Postcard Show (formerly BIPEX), held in late August at the Royal Horticultural Hall, SW1, while every weekend many smaller events are held regularly up and down the country. Here you will find the Postcard Trade at work, and will be able to meet the Dealers in person. Ask them for what you want, and you will find them all very helpful, particularly in guiding the new collector.

What to Collect
This depends entirely upon the individual. Visit the Fairs and look around at the enormous selection of cards you will find there. Perhaps after a few visits you may find yourself attracted to one particular Artist or Subject, or possibly you may wish to specialise in old views of your town or village. Whatever you choose, remember to look for cards in the finest possible condition. This is not perhaps so important in the Topographical field where only a few copies of a particular card may remain, but it is important in Art & Subjects. Generally you will want to ensure that the higher the price asked, the better the condition of the card.

How to Collect
At the Fairs. and in Dealers' advertisements, you will find a good range of accessories offered. Many collectors store their cards in albums, while others prefer loose storage in cardboard boxes. You may also consider it advisable to protect your loose cards by keeping them in protective envelopes now available. Some collectors prefer the old-fashioned Edwardian paper albums. rather than the modern PVC types. It is entirely up to you.

Postcard Clubs
As your interest grows, you may wish to join one of the many Postcard Clubs, a list of which may be found in Picture Postcard Annual. Here you will meet other local collectors who share your interest in the subject and who will be able to broaden your horizons by showing you some of their own collecting themes.

Investment
This is not something to be attempted by the new collector, for while it is always pleasant to see your collection grow in value, as indeed it will do, to set out to buy postcards with the sole aim of making money is an exercise fraught with difficulties. Wait until you know a lot more about the hobby. Then it may be possible to put some spare cash into an area you feel is under-valued, but a study of past Catalogues and past prices will clearly reveal that while some cards have risen dramatically in price, others have remained on the same mark for years, while some cards have even fallen in value.

Selling your Cards
All collectors wish to sell at different times. Perhaps they are giving up, or maybe turning to another subject. Whatever the reason, you have four basic methods of disposing of unwanted cards. You can take a table at one of the Postcard Fairs, and with your stock properly marked up and laid out, you can become a 'Dealer' yourself! If you know of other collectors in your field, you could offer your cards to them for sale by private treaty. Alternatively you can offer your stock to a dealer, but his response will depend very largely upon what sort of cards they are, their condition, and at the end of the day, whether he wants them! All cards must have a Catalogue value, but it does not necessarily follow that anyone wants to buy them! Most dealers will only willingly buy those cards in the collectable categories which they have some chance of re-selling at a profit. You can, of course, sell your cards on an internet auction site, which is readily available to everyone. Finally you can offer your cards for sale by Public Auction, but remember that here you take a chance on the final price. You may of course put a reserve on your cards, and if they fail to meet this figure they will be returned to you. You may be pleasantly surprised at the price you obtain at Auction, or in some cases you could be

disappointed. Certainly you may do better with particularly good single items if offered for sale by this method, but you have to meet the Auctioneer's commission, which may be up to 20% of the price realised. If you have a valuable collection, you may wish to discuss various methods of sale with an established Auctioneer or Dealer.

Modern Cards

The past 10 years has seen a phenomenal growth in the production of Modern postcards, and this can be seen as almost a separate industry, with cards on every conceivable subject now being issued by many leading companies. After some initial hesitation by the traditional postcard collecting world, Modern cards are now making considerable inroads into the hobby. Perhaps the great advantage of Modern Cards lies in their price, where for a nominal 50p, or so,one may buy superbly designed and printed cards on almost any subject you care to name.

Conclusions

In this brief survey we have tried to show how the hobby originated, and how it operates today. It is still growing, and I sincerely hope that all of you, particularly if you are a new collector finding out about postcards for the first time, will gain through this, and through the pages of this Catalogue, something of the nostalgia we collectors all feel for those long hot summer days at the turn of the century. It was for many a golden age, a time of faded sepia, and croquet on the lawns. Of knickerbocker suits, Sunday School and Mr. Polly, when the event of the year was annual trip to the seaside, with its toffee apples, winkles and busy, sad-eyed donkeys. A time of endless summer, when small boys looked for tiddlers under the bridge, oblivious to the voices calling them home across the fields, peacefully unaware of the later call of destiny which they would face in 1916 in the green fields of France.

A time without television, video, or computer games, when young girls and boys spent their evenings carefully putting all their new cards into their postcard albums. It is these cards which are so highly prized today, and which form the subject of this Catalogue.

ACCESSORY SUPPLIERS

Vera Trinder Ltd.
38 Bedford Street, London WC2 9EU   (See Page 12)   020-7257-9940

G. Barrington Smith*
Cross Street, Oadby, Leicester LE2 4DD   0116-271-9181

Sherford Stamp Co.
66 Bridge Street, Taunton, Somerset   01823-283327

Stanley Gibbons Publications
7 Parkside, Christchurch Road, Ringwood, Hampshire BH24 3SH   0800 611 622

Murray Cards International Ltd.
51 Watford Way, Hendon Central, London NW4 3JH   020-8202-5688

Rob Roy Cards
Crosshall, Chelsfield Village, Orpington, Kent   (See Page 11)   01689-828052

The firms listed above are trade wholesalers and between them carry an extensive range of Accessories including: Postcard Catalogues - Books - Albums - Leaves - Plastic Envelopes - Film Front Bags - Postcard Wallets etc.

Vera Trinder, G. Barrington Smith, and **Sherford Stamp Co.** also specialise in Philatelic and Numismatic albums and accessories, while **Murray Cards International** and **Rob Roy Cards** carry large stocks of Cigarette Card albums and leaves.

Most of the firms above will deal with individual customers, but a telephone call will confirm this, and determine whether the firm have the item you require currently in stock.

In addition many postcard dealers carry smaller stocks of Books, Albums and Accessories.

*Trade only supplied.

GLOSSARY OF POSTCARD TERMS

Applique
A term used to describe a postcard which has some form of cloth, metal, or other embellishment attached to it.

Art Deco
Artistic style of the 1920's recognisable by its symmetrical designs and straight lines.

Art Nouveau
Artistic style of the turn of the century, characterised by flowing lines and flowery symbols, yet often depicting impressionist more than representational art.

Bas Relief
Postcards with a heavily raised surface giving a papier-mache appearance.

Catch-phrases
Many pre-1914 Comic postcards are captioned by phrases such as "When Father says turn", often alluding to other spheres of contemporary life.

Chromo-Litho
The finest of all colour-printing methods, the colour being applied in solids as opposed to modern screen printing. There are no 'dots' in chromo-lithographic printing. Cards produced by this method have a rich and deep colour, where often the original shiny surface remains. Usually found in 'Gruss Aus' and other early undivided back cards.

Composites
A number of cards which together form a large picture.

Court Cards
The official size for British picture postcards between 1894-1899, measuring 115mm x 89mm.

Divided Back
Postcards with the back divided into two sections, one for the message, the other for the address. Great Britain first divided the back in 1902.

Early
A term loosely used to describe any undivided back card.

Embossed
Postcards with a raised surface. Often found among Greetings and Heraldic types.

Fab Cards
Produced by W.N. Sharpe of Bradford. These cards contain a small printed silk square which could be removed and used for other purposes.

Full out
Usually found in the Heraldic classification, meaning a design which fills the whole of the card.

Giant Postcards
Novelty cards, some of which were as large as 305mm x 165mm.

Glitter
Postcards sprinkled with tinsel.

Gruss Aus
German for "Greetings From". A term used to describe these highly pictorial continental Greetings Cards.

Hold to Light
Referred to as "HTL". Postcards with small cut out windows, through which appear different colours when held to a strong light.

Intermediate Size
The link between Court Cards and Standard Size, these were cards of 130mm x 80mm.

Kaleidoscopes
Postcards where a rotating wheel reveals a myriad of colours when turned.

Midget Postcards
Novelty cards of size 90mm x 70mm.

Montage
A term usually employed to describe a picture formed by cutting up postage stamps.

Novelty
A postcard which deviates in any way from the norm. Cards which do something or have articles attached to them, or are printed in an unusual size or on strange materials.

Official
Postcard printed by a Government or other established body to advertise their services. The Railway companies printed many 'Official' cards.

Oilette
A trade name used by the publishers Raphael Tuck to describe postcards reproduced from original paintings.

Panel Cards
These are postcards printed on heavy board.

Poster Advert
A reproduction of an advertising poster, or a postcard done specifically in that style.

Pullouts
Postcards containing a strip view insert.

Real Photographic
Abbreviated to 'R/P'. Used to describe a card which has been produced by a photographic rather than a printing process.

Reward Cards
Given away to reward school-children for good work.

Standard Size
Introduced in GB in November 1899, this size of 140mm x 89mm corresponds to 5.5 x 3.5 in.

Topographical
A term used to describe postcards showing street scenes and general views, where the view is more prominent than any other feature, e.g. if a Post Office or Public House were to form the dominant feature of a card, then it would be classified and priced under that heading.

Transparencies
Postcards which change colour or reveal a hidden object when held to a strong light.

Undivided Back
Postcards with a plain back where the whole of this space would be used for the address. A term often used loosely to describe Early Cards, although undivided backs were in common use until 1907.

Vignette
Usually found on undivided back postcards, and consisting of a design which does not occupy the whole of the picture side. Vignettes may be anything from a small sketch in one corner of the card, to a design covering three-quarters of the card. The essential idea was that some space should be left for the message, as the reverse of the card could only be used for the address.

Write-Away
A term used to describe a postcard bearing the opening line of a sentence, which the sender would then continue. Usually found on early Comic postcards.

THE PICTURE POSTCARD SHOW

LAWRENCE HALL
ROYAL HORTICULTURAL SOCIETY
Greycoat & Elverton Streets
LONDON SW1

THE EVENT of the YEAR

Top UK & International Dealers

Millions of Postcards for sale
from 1890's to present day

Accessories including albums,
protective covers and cases.

Free Postcard Valuations &
Advice for Collectors

Postcard Reference Books

Exhibition Displays

Collectors Postcard Club
Display Competition

FOR FUTURE DATES & FURTHER DETAILS CONTACT:
MIKE DAY 0151 339 5422 MELANIE MORDSLEY 0208 886 0469 DAVE DAVIS 01702 587603
or visit our website .... www.postcard.co.uk
2009 dates are yet to be confirmed at time of going to press

Postcard Traders Association
PROMOTING POSTCARDS THROUGH FAIR TRADING

Established in 1975. The Postcard Traders Association represents the UK's foremost dealers (and also many from overseas) auctioneers, fair organisers, publishers and accessory distributors amongst its members.

The principal aim of the 'PTA' is to promote postcards and the collecting hobby. Much of this work is carried out by the elected members and officers of the PTA committee, on a purely unpaid/voluntary basis, who are dedicated to ensuring a prosperous future for postcards and collecting. We also acknowledge other individuals, businesses and societies that assist us with our promotional work.

Membership of the PTA is open to anyone (over 18) who is in business trading in picture postcards or associated accessories. Members are vetted to ensure high standards in helping to protect the public against unfair or dubious trading practices.

For further information please contact our hon. secretary..
Derek Warry, 2 Millfield Park, Magor, Newport Gwent NP26 3LF
tel: 01633 880599 email: ptasecretary@postcard.co.uk

PLEASE VISIT OUR POSTCARD INFORMATION PAGES at www.postcard.co.uk

13

14

Bruce Bairnsfather - 1888-1959

Illustrator and cartoonist

Born in India he was the son of an Army officer. Joined the British Army in 1911 and served in France until 1910. He was wounded at Ypres but continued producing artworks.

Series 1;
Keeping his hand in.
There goes our blinkin' parapet again.
Better 'ole.
Things that matter.
Fatalist.
Obvious.

Series 2;
Coiffure in the trenches.
The eternal question.
The innocent abroad.
No possible doubt whatever.
That evening star-shell.
The thirst for reprisal.

COIFFURE IN THE TRENCHES
"Keep yer 'ead still, or I'll 'ave yer blinkin' ear off."

Series 3;
Directing the way at the front.
Our democratic army.
The tactless Teuton.
That sword.
They've evidently seen me.
Where did that one go to?

Series 4;
A.D. nineteen fifty.
Gott strafe this barbed wire.
A Maxim Maxim.
"The Push" - in three chapters.
Vacant situation.

Series 5;
Peace___, At present we are staying at a farm.
The ideal and the real.
In and Out 1.
In and Out 11.
- these - rations.
- Watch me make a fire-bucket of 'is 'elmet.

Series 6;
Adaptable armies.
That 16 inch sensation.
Same old moan.
What it really feels like.
Dream.
Night-time patrol.

Series 7;
The concientious exhilarator.
My dreams for years to come.
The historical touch.
Springtime in Flanders.
The dud shell - or fuse top collector.
When one would like to start an offensive of one's own

Series 8;
Happy memories of the zoo.
Trouble with one of the souvenirs.
The nest.

Series 9;
The Intelligence department
The communication trench
Observation
Nobbled
The secret sorrow
Dual Obsession

CAPT. BRUCE BAIRNSFATHER, noanuar no THE BRILLIANT ARTIST WHOSE HUMOROUS SERIES OF WAR DRAW- "FRAGMENTS FROM FRANCE" ARE KNOWN AND APPRECIATE THROUGHOUT THE BRITISH EMPIRE.

THE SOLDIER'S DREAM
A "Bitter" disappointment on waking.

IN AND OUT (II)
That first half-hour after "coming out" of the trenches.

"Bystanders" Fragments From France
Series 1-6 £2.50-£7.
Series 7-9 £5-9
Theatre £18-£25.

BLOOMSBURY
POSTCARD & EPHEMERA FAIR

In the Galleon Suite at **The Royal National Hotel**
Bedford Way, London WC1

90 PACKED TABLES EVERY MONTH

Come along and find some spectacular cards

2008 Sundays:
SEPTEMBER 28TH
OCTOBER 26TH
NOVEMBER 23RD
DECEMBER 21ST

2009 Sundays:
January 25th
February 15th
March 22nd
April 26th
May 24th
June 28th
July 26th
August 23rd
September 27th
October 25th
November 22nd
December 20th

POSTCARDS,
EPHEMERA,
AUTOGRAPHS, MOVIE
JUMBLE, SPORTING
MEMORABILIA,
PRINTS, SCRAPS,
PROGRAMMES,
PHOTOGRAPHS,
CIGARETTE CARDS,
TRADE CARDS,
CARTE DE VISITES,
STEREOCARDS,
POSTAL HISTORY,
MAGAZINES,
BOOKS, POSTERS,
ACCESSORIES Etc;

Open 10 a.m. to 4.30p.m.
Admission £1.50 (Incl. FREE postcard)
Early entry available at 8.00 a.m.

I P M PROMOTIONS
130 Brent St, Hendon, London NW4.
Tel , 020 8202 9080 020 8203 1500
Fax 020 8203 7031
e-mail dave@memoriespostcards.co.uk
www.memoriespostcards.co.uk

WHAT THE PRICES MEAN

With a few exceptions, all cards in this Catalogue have been given a single price, representing a broad average figure for the majority of cards in their respective classification. For example:

ART and SUBJECT CARDS

The stated price may be taken as a broad average figure for all Art and Subject cards. You will find C.E. Flower listed at £2. There are many common cards by this artist which are worth no more than £1, while his rare cards would certainly be worth £3. The great bulk of his output therefore would be expected to sell at the broad average figure of £2.

TOPOGRAPHICAL and SOCIAL HISTORY

With any relevant entry, e.g. Motor Bus . Tram . Street Market . Windmill etc. the stated price, or broad average figure, is for a card, *either RP or Printed, fully identified and showing a 'Close-up at a named location'*, with real photographic cards being the most desirable. (Logically it will be appreciated that to qualify for listing at all, a Bus or Tram etc. has to be a *"Close-up"* in the first place and as such would represent the *majority of cards in that classification*). Generally speaking, anything less would be classified as a street scene at a lower price. If you think of a Bus or Tram in the middle distance, that is a street scene, while a Windmill in the middle-distance would similarly be priced at a lower figure.

With this in mind, it is then necessary to apply certain other criteria before formulating a final price, as with all Topographical and Social History cards, it is neither realistic nor practical to subdivide each entry into considerations of: Real Photographic . Printed . Close-up . Far Distance . Located . Unlocated . Identified . Unidentified . Common . Scarce . Publisher . Condition etc., not to mention whether the card is in a saleable area or even if it forms part of a remaindered stock! (You will begin to appreciate the problems in pricing these cards!). Put simply, the card has to be a Close-up to qualify for the price given. Consideration of all these other factors will then enable you to arrive at a final valuation.

A real photographic Motor Bus is catalogued at £35. A distant view of a Bus trundling along a country road may fetch £5, while a common, mass produced card of Buses in Trafalgar Square would only be worth 50p. On the other hand, a spectacular real photograph of a bus in a provincial town, taken by a local photographer, where the image fills the whole of the card, may fetch £50. Real Photographic cards are generally worth more than Printed cards, but a middle distance RP would be worth less than a superb Printed close-up. Admittedly, this is not easy for collectors new to the hobby, but as you gain more knowledge you will quickly see how it all works! Pricing is not an exact science, nor would we ever wish it to be!

It is further pointed out that in all relevant classifications, 'Accidents' would carry a price toward the higher end of the scale.

FURTHER INFORMATION

It must always be borne in mind that an exceptional card or complete set in any classification may fetch a price well in excess of Catalogue valuation. There are many reasons for this. In the dealer's stock any particularly rare or desirable item may be felt to be worth a premium, given the number of potential buyers, while at auction the same card, or complete set, would be offered to a totally different world-wide clientele, with a resulting number of high bids being received. It does not therefore follow that any auction realisation can be taken as representing current market value as perceived by the majority of dealers throughout the country.

In many Subject classifications, for example, Animals, Children, Greetings etc. one finds many cards printed by the early chromo-litho method. The superior quality of these cards would put them at the higher end of the price range.

It is not possible to be more specific given the huge numbers and types of postcards produced, neither is it realistic to have an entry for 'Chromo-Litho' under hundreds of Subject listings!

A single figure has been for all classifications where the majority of cards are of similar content, e.g. Bamforth Song Cards. One would expect to find such cards in any dealer's stock, priced at around the stated price.

The Price Range has been retained for classifications where one finds a wide divergence of content in available cards, e.g. 'Advert Cards/Poster Type'. Here only knowledge and experience can be your guide, though it is quite practical to take a middle average price for any particular card. This will enable you to form a realistic assessment of the value of your collection.

Unless otherwise stated, all cards in this catalogue are priced as being commercially published. Private and family photographs have no value other than what they may be worth to a particular collector. There are certain exceptions e.g. 'Contemporary Fashion, Weddings' and similar collectable cards.

Unless clearly stated in the text, all prices are for single cards.

In all cases, prices are for cards in fine condition, with no marks or bent corners etc. This is particularly so with Art and Subject cards, whereas in the Topographical and Social History fields, the image may be felt to outweigh considerations of condition.

The cards listed in this Catalogue are with very few exceptions pre-1939 and all standard size 5.5 x 3.5 in. This date may be extended to 1945 for the issues of World War 2, and as far as 1970 for GB Topographical Views, Civil Aviation, Cinema and one or two other subjects as indicated in the listings.

Certain issues in the larger 6 x 4 size did occur during this period, and are listed as appropriate, but with the odd exception, this Catalogue does not concern itself with anything later than 1970 in either size.

All prices in this Catalogue, many of them covering thousands of cards with one figure, must be taken as a broad average of that particular classification. Please do not say "PPV gives £3 for this". PPV does not give £3 for this. PPV suggests £3 as a mean average figure for the majority of cards of that type. Some cards may be worth £1, while others may be worth £5. Please bear this in mind when buying or selling.

N.B. It must be pointed out to non-collectors wishing to sell cards, that perhaps 75% of all postcards are virtually worthless! Postcards are like Stamps or Coins, in that huge quantities of common, or low-denomination material exists in today's market. I refer to Greetings cards - Landscapes - Seasides - Tourist Areas - Churches - Cathedrals - common Foreign views etc. All these cards are catalogued, and all must have a price, but it does not follow that anyone wants to buy them! Such cards may be picked up from auctions or trade sources in bulk at nominal cost. Effectively, what dealers want to buy are the better cards catalogued at £1.50 and upwards, which they can sell again. Please bear this in mind when offering cards for sale.

MODERN CARDS

As a brief guide it can be assumed that while certain subject themes may have a value of up to several pounds each, the vast majority of subject cards can be purchased new for 50p or less and secondhand or used for a few pence each.

As for topographical views, the same price structure applies, although it is pointed out to prospective vendors that views of foreign holiday areas are worth very little.

ARTISTS / COLLECTIONS

The years at the turn of the century saw the production of a number of selected postcard series, now justly celebrated as representing the high-water mark of postcard art and design. In this respect France was very much to the fore, and I give below a list of these series, together with details of other leading European collections. This is almost entirely the province of the European collector, for although these cards do come along from time to time in our Auctions, the interest in Britain is limited to a few people.

Market Report
A highly specialised area which has seen steady interest, prices tend to be determined at auction, generally outside the scope of the UK market.
Present price ranges are considered adequate.

AUSTRIA
WIENER WERKSTATTE 1908-1913
Recognised by the title design on the reverse, these cards were produced perhaps as a reaction to the swirling lines of Art Nouveau, being typified by a spare and severe style which gave way to Cubism and Art Deco. Artists include: Mela Koehler and Oskar Kokoschka.
Price Range: £50/750

FRANCE
COCORICO
Probably the most celebrated of all French series. There are 12 designs only. Artists include: De Feure and Steinlen.
Price Range: £150/£750

COLLECTION DES CENT. 1901
A series of 100 cards by leading Artists of the day. Cards have this title printed at the edge. Artists include: Alphonse Mucha, Caran d'Ache, Jules Cheret and A. Steinlen.
Price Range: £50/£500

COLLECTION JOB 1895-1914
There were three series together totalling 78 cards. Reprints of calendars and posters from the period above. Artists include: Angelo Asti, Jules Cheret and Alphonse Mucha.
Price Range: £50/£300

CONCOURS DE BYRHH 1906
A competition held to select advertisements for this aperitif. 113 designs were published as postcards. Artists include: Maurice Denis, Raphael Kirchner and G. Meunier.
Price Range: £50/£300

EDITIONS CINOS 1898
A series of 35 cards by famous artists of the day. Artists include: Alphonse Mucha, Jules Cheret, and Toulouse-Lautrec.
Price Range: £100/750

GERMANY
JUGEND 1899
Three series totalling 75 cards, in the Art Nouveau style. Artists include: Hans Christiansen.
Price Range: £50/£300

BAUHAUS 1923.
This series consisted of 20 designs, with reputedly only about 25 copies of each design printed. Artists include: Paul Klee and Kurt Schmidt.
Price Range: £250/£2500

CHROMO-LITHO

Generally acknowledged as the finest of all colour printing methods. Briefly, the design was etched onto a limestone block and printed in solid colours, as opposed to modern screen printing, where the dots can be seen through a strong glass. Chromo-Litho printing was used extensively for postcards from 1890-1910, particularly in the 'Gruss Aus' and 'Early Vignette' classifications. The reader is directed to the specialist books in this field which will list many of the hundreds of publishers engaged in this form of printing.The price of any Chromo-Litho card may be found by reference to its subject or artist, but there exist a great many unsigned Chromo-Litho cards of general landscape type.

ART REPRODUCTIONS

Friezes/Red Border types	£2
Miscellaneous reproductions	£1

Chromo-Litho/Heavy Board

Misch & Stock/Sborgi/Stengel	£2

Gallery Reproduction Series

Photochrom Co.	.75

Early Chromo Litho printed card Como by Manuel Wielandt £8

Chromo Litho, Tuck's English Cathedrals £6

TOPOGRAPHICAL ART

In recent years the collection of chromo-litho topographical art has become popular in its own right. Prominent names in this field include Manuel Wielandt, Michael Zeno Diemer, Raoul Frank, Paul Kley, K. Mutter and A. Prosnocimi. These and others are listed in the main Artist index.

Many cards in this genre however are unsigned, and a guide to the price of these is given below:

French Views	£3
Italian Views	£3
Swiss Views	£3
Other countries	£3

ART TYPES

Colouring Cards/Pairs

Tuck R. & Sons	£2
Miscellaneous Types	£1

Oilfacism

Tuck R. & Sons	£1.50
Miscellaneous Oil Facsimiles	£1

Hand Painted

Professional Work	£5
Amateur Work	£2
Mass produced	£1

SCULPTURE

Art Sculpture on black card	£1
Gallery/Museum types	.75

Montage scenes

Mastroianni D.	£2

ART DECO

Art Deco remains an important postcard classification, reflecting as it does the work of many leading artists of the twentieth century. Art Deco began in the early years after 1900, as a reaction to the swirling and complex designs of Art Nouveau. The style was characterised by a more severe and economical line, and was later to be inspired by cubism. It reached its height in 1925 with the Paris Exposition des Arts Decoratifs et Modernes, but died out in the 1930s. At its peak, the Art Deco style reached into many other branches of the arts, and its influence was particularly notable in the design of contemporary architecture, furniture and fashion. The `Odeon' cinemas of the period are a typical example. Artist signed postcards are difficult to price accurately while unsigned work can only sell for what the buyer is prepared to pay.

Much current business is conducted through the auction rooms where this subject always sells well, with the better artists much in demand.

*Left: Art Deco £15
Right; Chiostri £25
Bottom right: Mela
Koehler £70,
Bottom Left:
Meschini £35*

ART NOUVEAU

This is a highly specialised field which, like Art Deco, reaches into the Fine Art World, with the consequent high price structure of many of its Artists. Typified by a swirling, flowing style, Art Nouveau reached its apogee at the turn of the century in the work of Mucha, Kirchner and Basch, among others, but died out about ten years later. Like Art Deco, the postcards are

difficult to price, for although the style is quite popular with British collectors, most business today is conducted through the auction houses selling single cards, often at widely differing figures. It is fair to say however, that considerable opportunities remain for the informed collector, whose specialised knowledge may be used to advantage at postcard fairs or retail outlets. The work of top artists is keenly sought by an exclusive clientele, with much interest coming from the USA and the Continent. Both Art Nouveau and Art Deco, however, remain a rather heady mix for the average British collector.

Left; A K Macdonald £35
Below Left: Henri Meunier £95
Bottom Left: Tuck's 2709 Kirchner £60
Below Right; Typical Art Nouveau £35

RAPHAEL KIRCHNER

Kirchner was born in Vienna in 1875 and died in America at the height of his fame in 1917. His work dates from 1897 to 1916 and during this time he produced nearly 800 postcard designs, grouped together in over 120 sets and other issues, published by some 77 separate firms. Kirchner was one of the leading figures in the Art Nouveau movement, although some of his later work lay more in the field of straight Glamour. His cards have been catalogued by Antonio and Pia Dell'Aquila in,"Raphael Kirchner and his Postcards" published in 1996. This magisterial work illustrates every known card and gives a full listing of all known publishers. Readers who wish to look further into the life and work of this great artist can have no better guide. All one can do within the confines of a general catalogue such as this, is give a brief guide to those cards which by reason of publisher or other factors, are most often found on the British market, together with an indication of price. This in itself can only be a very broad assessment, as many of these series were reprinted by other publishers, often in different formats, with added greetings or other variations. It is further noted that certain rare cards not listed here, can be worth anything up to £500+ each. One problem remains with Kirchner in that some of his cards are unsigned. There is not much we can do about this other than refer the reader to Dell'Aquila where every card is identified. What follows is merely a general guide which I hope will be of some help to collectors.

All prices below are for single cards. A complete set may attract a premium over this figure. It must be noted that prices apply to cards in flawless condition, with no marks or damage of any kind. With highly rated cards such as these, condition is everything and those in less than perfect state would be worth considerably less.

'Raphael Kirchner and his Postcards' may be purchased from: Reflections of a Bygone Age, 15 Debdale Lane, Keyworth, Notts. NG12 5HT at the price of £29.95 including postage.

A Quatre Feuilles Set 6		£65
Girls' heads in clover leaf		
Enfants de la Mer Set 10		£65
Girls at the Seaside		
Fruits Douces Set 6		£65
Girls with fruit between green borders		
Geisha Set 10		£40
Scenes of Japanese life		
Greek Virgins Set 12		£65
Girls in beige & gold design		
See also Tuck Listing		
Les Cigarrettes du Monde Set 6		£65
Girls smoking cigarettes		
Maid of Athens Set 6+		
Studies of young girls		
Coloured		£40
Bw series		£25
See also Tuck listing		
Mikado Set 6		£50
Japanese Girls		

Santoy Set 6		£60
Scenes of Japanese Life		
Demi Vierge Set 6		£65
Girls on gold background between green borders		
Femmes Soleil Set 6		£65
Girls' faces on background of sunrays		
Same designs on pale blue without sunrays		
Erika Set 6		£65
Girls' heads on floral background		
Marionettes Set 6		£65
Girls with puppets		
Bijoux Set 6		£65
Girls in goblet/heart shaped panels		
Les Peches Capitaux Set 7		£35
Girl with inset pierrot head		
Kirchner Girls Set 24		£25
Bruton Galleries		
Delta Fine Art Co. EC2		
Kirchner Girls Set 12		£25
Bruton Galleries		
Alphalsa Publishing Co. EC2		
Les Amours de Pierrot Set 10		£35
Girl with inset pierrot head on titled card		
Reinthal & Newman/New York		
Librairie de l'Estampe/Paris		£35
Glamour/WW1 period. 32 cards		
Numbered and titled on back		

Cards published in Britain by Raphael Tuck & Sons.

Connoisseur 2555
Salome
Girls' large faces with scenic background
Coloured   Set 6   £60
Black & White   Set 6   £30

Connoisseur 2642
Les Ephemeres   Set 6   £100
Three girls in flowing dresses

Oilette Connoisseur 2709
Flashing Motorists   Set 6   £60

Continental 3002   Set 6   £85
Continental 3003   Set 6   £85
Girls' faces in circle with
mauve background

Continental 3004   Set 10   £85
Continental 3005   Set 10   £85
Girls standing in Flowers

Continental 4002
Continental 4003
Maid of Athens
Coloured   Set 6   £40
Black & White   Set 6   £25

Continental 4008   Set 6   £85
Continental 4009   Set 6   £85
Girls in panels with pink borders

Continental 4016   Set 6   £85
Continental 4017   Set 6   £85
Girls in panels with olive borders

Continental 4024   Set 6   £65

Continental 4025   Set 6   £65
Greek Virgins

Diaphne 3501   Set 5   £200
Diaphne 8902   Set 5   £200
Vitraux d'Art
Girls in stained glass windows

The postcards of Raphael Kirchner can be
divided into three main periods:
The Early Beginnings: 1897 - 1899
The Golden Age: 1900 - 1907
The Glamour Age: 1910 - 1917

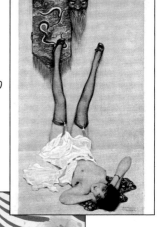

Above; Girl in goblet shaped panel . £60

Right;
Le masque impassible. £40

Femmes Soleil. £65

ADVERTISING

One of the most popular and widely collected postcard themes. Many different types of Advertising cards were produced during the early years of this century, both by the companies whose products they advertised, and by the independent publishers. They range from the very attractive 'Poster Types', designed in the form of an advertising poster, or sometimes reproducing an established poster such as Fry's classic 'Five Boys' design, to the many plainer types known as 'Giveaways'. These were published by the company for promotional purposes, and were often given away with the product, although many more do show themes such as the gathering, processing, or manufacture of the product. Companies across the whole spectrum of industry produced Advertising cards of one sort or another, and we have cards from the Food and Drink industry, Animal Feed Manufacturers, Newspapers and Magazines, the Tobacco Industry, and many more. In addition, many of the Railway and Shipping companies, as well as other more specialised issues are listed under those respective sections. We also include 'Reward Cards' under the main entry, as these were given away to school-children for good attendance.

Market Report
This is one area that has not benefited from sales on the internet and where it is difficult to differentiate reproductions from the genuine article. Out of favour as a theme these days.

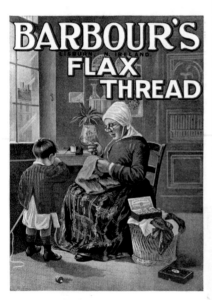

HIS ONLY PAIR.

Barbour's Flax thread £28

Bass Chromo Litho £35

Pratts Motor Oil £30

POSTER TYPE

Beecham's Pills
Tom Browne designs   £25

Beer & Baccy
Victoria State 1896   £30

Berry's Boot Polish   £20

Bird's Custard   £20

British Army
Recruiting Poster   £30

Bryant & May   £35

Cadbury's   £40

Camp Coffee
Harry Payne designs   £60
Other designs   £30

Campbell's Soups
G. Weidersheim designs   £25

Capern's Bird Foods   £15

Cerebos Salt   £25

Champion Vinegar   £12

Claymore Whiskey
Defenders of the Empire   £10

Continental Tyres   £25

C.W.S
Pelaw Metal Polish   £18
Other Products   £18

Epps Milk Chocolate   £25

Fletcher's Sauce   £25
GP Government Tea   £15

Gossage's Soap   £25

Heinz H.J. & Co.   £18

H.P. Sauce   £30

Horniman's Tea   £25

Hudson's Soap   £25

James Keiller   £15

John Knight Soap   £25

Mustad Horse Nails   £25

Nestle's Milk   £30

North British Rubber Co.   £30

Ovaltine   £15

Palmer Tyres   £25

Peek Frean
Tom Browne designs   £25

Raleigh Cycles   £30

Schweppes   £12

Horniman's Tea   £25

Skipper Sardines   £10

Wood Milne Rubber Heels   £15

Miscellaneous Products   £10/£30

Suchard Chocolate/Cocoa
One of the earliest companies to employ the medium of the picture postcard for advertising purposes, Suchard were producing cards from c.1890 onwards.

Early Vignette/Gruss Aus type   £20

SETS & SERIES

C.W.S. Packet Teas
Dickens sketches/Trade back	£8
Time Around the World/Trade back	£10

Epps Cocoa
Nature series	£8

Famous Posters in Miniature
H.M.& Co.	£30

GP Government Tea
Set 6/KEVII at Windsor
Price per set	£130

Lemco
Coronation series	£15
Types of Lemco Cattle	£10

Quaker Oats
Smiles/Set 10	£12

Shell Oil
Original series	£35
Reproductions	.50

Walker, Harrison & Garthwaite
Phoenix Poultry Foods	£10
Viscan Pet Foods	£10
VC Winners	£12

For other Advertising cards on Aviation, Motoring, Railway, Shipping and Theatrical, please see those headings.

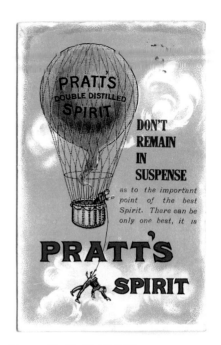

Above; Pratt's Spirit £ 35

CHROMO-LITHO

Standard-size cards, mainly of French origin, and printed Chromo-Litho, usually in early vignette style. They carry the brand name of a product on an often quite unrelated design.

Arlatte Chicory
Tuck R. & Sons/Flowers	£10

Belle Jardiniere
Art sketches	£20

Chocolat Lindt
Children/Art sketches	£20

Chocolat Lombart
Children/Art sketches	£20

Lipton
Language of Flowers	£18

Scott's Emulsion
French Departments/Set 92	£8

COURT SIZE

These are among the earliest examples of Advertising cards. Smaller than standard postcard size, and usually printed chromo-litho in vignette style.

Hutchinson Novels
Literary adverts	£25

Johnston's Corn Flour
Some Methods of Travelling/Set 24	£35

Nestle's Swiss Milk
Military vignettes	£40

St. Ivel Cheese | £20 |

FRIENDLY SOCIETIES

Not exactly Poster Type, although some very attractive designs may be found on these cards.

Grand United Order of Oddfellows	£6
Hearts of Oak Benefit Society	£6
Independent Order of Rechabites	£6

Order of the Sons of Temperance
Heraldic Designs	£6
Bridges/Castles/Churches	£10

Twentieth Century Equitable
Friendly Society	£6

POSTER TYPE/SERIES

FRY J.S. & SONS

Prices

As with Tuck Celebrated Posters, a wide divergence exists in the current market value of these cards. Some are very common, others remarkably scarce.

Tom Browne designs	£15/£30
With Capt Scott at the South Pole	£50
Other designs	£20/£40

Caption	Artist
Showcard Replica Series	
What's good for the bee	
His heart's desire	
A perfect dream	
The tired traveller	
On the top	
A perfect food	
Sweeter than honey	

Vivian Mansell &Co.

Unapproachable	
This is my brother Billy	
A source of delight	
Is the best	
Keeps out the cold	

Various Publishers

John Bull says support home industries	R.C. Carter
Cow being milked	R.C. Carter
The prize winner	Chas. Pears
If you feel cold	Chas. Pears
My eye! Ain't Fry's Chocolate nice	Chas. Pears
Far too good to share	Chas. Pears
The diver's lucky find	
Cocoa Sah!	Edgar Filby
Good old mater	
Fry's Milk Chocolate (White Cow)	
A perfect breakfast table	
Fry's Milk Chocolate (Pyjama boy)	
With Capt. Scott at the South Pole	
Keeps out the cold	
No better food after a good bath	Maud Fabian
The five senses	
Five girls want	
Always merry and bright	Ernest Noble
Great Scott! What a find.	John Hassall
Avec les compliments	
Disgraced but not defeated	Edgar Filby
I fully endorse	
I am ... etc.	
Yes, it's Fry's	
It's worth the risk	
Unrivalled ... etc.	
A double first	
The bloom of health	
No better food	
Design as above/C.W. Faulkner	
The little connoisseur	
Over the top and the best of luck	
Fry's for good	
So near and yet so far	Tom Browne
Highway robbery	Tom Browne
See their eyes as she buys	
Fry's	Tom Browne
One touch of nature	Tom Browne
Right up to date	Tom Browne
Fry's Cocoa (rich girl)	Tom Browne
Hello Daddy	
Whom God preserve	
Compliments of J.S. Fry & Sons Ltd.	
Fry's Coca (Boy with train)	
Fry's Chocolate for endurance	
Well, if you know of a better cocoa!	
Going by leaps and bounds	
Jolly good for the money	
Sustaining and invigorating	
Fry's, it's good	
The best is good enough for me	
Fry's Pure Cocoa/ Design as above/J.S. Fry & Sons Ltd.	
Tuck CP 1500	Gordon Browne
Fry's Milk Chocolate/Tuck CP 1502	

TUCK R. & SONS
Celebrated Posters

Prices

There exists a considerable variance in price for these cards, even for the same card, if sold at auction or by a dealer. Basically the lower numbered series are the more common, and would range from about £15-£30 depending upon the artist, design, product, condition etc. But even here we find particular cards occurring more frequently than the others. Indeed some are positively commonplace!

The higher series from 1504 onwards are less often found, with the contrary position that certain cards seem almost non-existent! Here the price range would be from £30-£75, although prices as high as £150 for particular cards have been noted in the stocks of certain dealers.

For a more comprehensive study of this subject we recommend 'The Picture Postcards of Raphael Tuck & sons'. by J.H.D.Smith.

TOBACCO

A special classification for these cards reflects a shared interest with the cigarette card world

Adkins Tobacco
Tom Browne posters .... £150+

Cavander's Army Mixture
Poster type £25

Dimitrino Cigarettes
Chromo-Litho £15

Gallaher's Park Drive Cigarettes
Poster type £12

Gitanes Cigarettes
Poster type/Art Deco £30

Godfrey Phillips
Set 30/Beauty Spots of the Homeland £8
Set 24/Coronation Series £8
Set 26/Famous Paintings £8
Set 24/Film Stars £60
Set 48/Film Stars £60
Set 30/Garden Studies £6
Set 12/Jubilee Series £6
Set 30/Our Dogs £90
Set 30/Our Glorious Empire £12
Set 30/Our Puppies £40

Grapevine Cigarettes
Southend Lifeboat 1906 .... £15

Gray's Cigarettes
Views £3

Job Cigarette Papers
Vercasson/Poster type:
Chromo-Litho £50
Early vignettes £25

Lea R. & J./Chairman Cigarettes
O.E. Pottery and Porcelain/Set 24 .... £6
With supplier's imprint £8

Mitchell's Prize Crop
Glasgow Exhibition 1901 .... £75

Murad Turkish Cigarettes £30

Nicholas Sarony
Film Stars £3

Ogden's
Poster type £90

Players
Poster type £75
Other types £30

Sandorides Lucana Cigarettes
Poster type £20

JOB Cigarette Papers   *£40*

U.K. Tobacco Co./The Greys
Beautiful Britain £2

Wills W.D. & H.O.
Poster type: Capstan/Gold Flake/
Three Castles/Westward Ho! £100

Miscellaneous Companies
Poster type .... £15/£40
Views etc. .... £2+

Charlesworth & Austin cigarette advert   *£40*

GIVE AWAY/INSERT CARDS

This section covers those cards given away or distributed by commercial firms, newspapers and magazines, etc., for promotional purposes. Subjects depicted are varied, and often have no relation to the product advertised. Here again the total number of firms who produced these cards is incalculable. We list below the more common and collectable cards.

Amami Shampoo	
Prichard & Constance	£2
Answers	£4
Bazaar, Exchange & Mart	
Comic sketches	£8
Beecham's Pills	
GB views	£1
Bees Ltd.	£1
Bensdorp Cocoa	
Pierrots	£12
Dutch Scenes	£3
London views	£1.50
Isle of Marken	£1
Books/Magazines/Newspapers	
Military/Mail/Front Page	£3
French Newspapers/Front Page	£3
Other publications	£3
Boon's Cocoa	
European views	.75
Bovril	
Art Reproductions	£1
Brett's Publications	
GB views	£1.50
British Dominions Insurance	
Art studies/Set 24	£1.50
Bromo Cocoa	
Plantation sketches	£2
Brooke Bond	
Silhouettes of Manchester	£12
Butywave Shampoo	
Film Stars	£3
Cadbury Bros.	
Bournville village	£1.50
Canadian Dept. of Emigration	
Canadian views	£1.50
Canary and Cage Bird Life	
Cage Bird Studies/32 cards	
/pc back	£5
/trade back	£3

Capern's Bird Foods	
Cage bird studies/pc back	£3
/trade back	£1.50
Captain Magazine	
Tom Browne sketches	£8
Carter Paterson	
Art sketches	£2
Carter's Seeds	£1.50
Chelsea Flower Show	£3
Chick's Own	£5
Chivers & Sons	
Studies of English Fruits	£2
Aerial views of Histon	£2
Christian Novels	
GB views	£1.50
Colman's Starch	
Postmen of the Empire	£12
GB sketches	£3
Connoisseur	
Art Reproductions	.50
Cook E./Lightning Series	
Aviation studies	£8
Crawford's Cream Crackers	
Russo-Japanese war map 1905	£8
CWS Soaps	£5
Daily Chronicle	
Fashion adverts	£5
Daily Express	£2
Daily Mirror	
Fair of Fashions Competition	£2
Beauty Contest	£2
Daily News/Wallet Guide	
GB views	£1.50
Daily Sketch	
The Daily Sketch Girl	£3
Dainty Novels	
Greetings/Coloured	£2
Other subjects	£1.50
De Beukelaer's Cocoa	
Topographical sketches	.75
Dewar's Whisky	
Gems of Art series	£1.50
Eagle Insurance Co.	
Head Office building	£4
Elliman's Linament	
Tuck R. & Sons	£5
Family Reader	
Various subjects	£1.50

My GOODNESS –
My GUINNESS

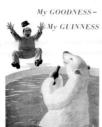

Bottle Royal

Why was the Hatter mad?

GUINNESS
FOR STRENGTH

GUINNESS IS GOOD FOR YOU

GUINNESS
FOR STRENGTH

GUINNESS IS GOOD FOR YOU

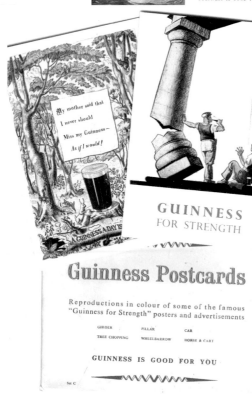

My mother said that
I never should
Miss my Guinness –
As if I would!

GUINNESS
FOR STRENGTH

Guinness Postcards

Reproductions in colour of some of the famous
"Guinness for Strength" posters and advertisements

GIRDER	PILLAR	CAR
TREE CHOPPING	WHEELBARROW	HORSE & CART

GUINNESS IS GOOD FOR YOU

Set C

My GOODNESS –
My GUINNESS

Above; **Guinness Postcards** *£ 8 each.*
3 sets of six cards produced on heavy card
and larger size 6" x 4" with an envelope.

Set A. features Alice in Wonderland.
Alice Studies Natural History
Mushroom Growth
Why was the Hatter Mad
Bottle & Jug
My Mother Said....
Bottle Royal.

Set B. features Animal Posters.
Lion & Keeper
Pelican
Kangaroo & Keeper
Sea Lion & Keeper
Polar Bear
Toucan.

Set C. features "Guiness for Strength"
Posters.
Girder
Pillar
Car
Tree Chopping
Wheelbarrow
Horse & Cart

Feathered World
Poultry studies £5

Field J.C./Toilet Soaps
Childhood sketches £4

Field The
Military sketches £4

Fine Arts Publishing Co.
Burlington Proofs .75

F-M-N Complete Novels
Theatrical portraits £1.50

Formosa Oolong Tea
Sketches on Rice Paper £10
Japanese prints £3

Fry J.S. & Sons
Non-poster types £8
Views of Somerdale Works £2

Garden City Association
Letchworth Garden City/
   Set 12/Frank Dean £4
   Set 6/W.W. Ratcliffe £4

Gentlewoman
Royal Artist Post Card Series £4

Girl's Own Paper
Art sketches/4 designs £10

Glaxo
Various subjects £3

Goss W.H.
Oates S. & Co. £8

Guinness A.
Cartoons/6x4 size/
Three sets of 6 cards (per card) £8
Brewery scenes £8
Brewery scenes/6x4 size £4

Harland & Wolf
Valentine & Sons £6

Hartley W.P.
Jam production scenes £2

Haydock Coals
Art Reproduction/GB views £1

Health and Strength
Physical Culture studies £8
Hoffman's Starch £1.50

Home Words
Various subjects £1.50

Horner's Penny Stories
Various subjects £3

Horniman's Tea
Invisible Picture £8
GB views £2

Hotels/Restaurants
GB/Artist sketches £3
GB Photographic/Printed £5
Foreign/Gruss Aus type £3
Foreign/Later issues £1

Ideas Weekly
The Imps £8

Idle Moments
Various subjects £1.50

Imperial Fine Art Corporation
Art Reproductions .75

International Horse Show £8

Jacob W. & R.
Biscuit production scenes £3

King Insurance Co.
GB Royalty sketches £6

Lever Bros.
Port Sunlight village £1.50

Liberty's £8

Liebig Fray-Bentos
Oxo Shackleton Expedition £25
Meat processing scenes £4

Lipton
Tea Estate sketches £1.50

Liverpool, China & India Tea Co. Ltd.
Atlantic Liners £15

Lord Mayor Treloar Home
Institution scenes £1.50

Maggi
European views .75

Manchester Dock & Harbour Board
Topographical sketches £6

Mazawattee Tea & Chocolate
Louis Wain Cats/Postcard £85
   /Trade Back £50

Mellin's Food
Costume & Flags/Set 12 £6
Various subjects £6

Melox
Animal Foods £6

Menier Chocolate
Paris sketches £1

Miniature Novels
Various subjects £1.50

Mirror Novels
Theatrical/Bookmark type £3

Molassin Meal/Dog Cakes
Various subjects £8

My Pocket Novel
Various subjects £1.50

My Queen & Romance
Various subjects   £1.50

Nestle's
Animals & Birds/3rd 1?   £U

New Zealand Govt. Department
Topographical sketches   £1.50

New Zealand Lamb
Dairy Farming scenes   .75

North British Rubber Co.
Golfing sketches   £45

Norwich Union
Motor Fire Engine   £12

Ocean Accident & Guarantee Corp.
Insurance Post Card Series   £4

Odol Dentifrice
Actresses   £4

Oetzmann's Cottages
Exhibition cards   £1.50

Old Calabar
Animal Foods   £10

Oliver Typewriters
Writing through the Ages   £6

Overprints
Advertising copy overprinted on to otherwise standard commercial postcard. Value as latter plus nominal premium.

Oxo
Oxo Cattle Studies   £15

Peark's Butter/Tea
Various subjects   £2

Pears A. & F.
Various subjects   £2
Bubbles   £1

Peek Frean
Invisible Picture   £10
CB views   £2

Pickfords
Transport sketches   £8
Reproductions   .50

Pitman Health Food Co.
Ideal food series   £5

Postcard Connoisseur
Dore's London/1904 Facsimile   £50

Price's Candles
Military sketches   £8
Nursery Riddles   £8

Princess Novels
Various subjects   £1.50

Red Letter/Red Star Weekly
Greetings/Coloured   £3

Norwich Union Advert £12

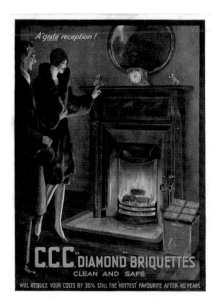

CCC Diamond Briquettes £14

The all British 12/24
Standard
"Park Lane" Saloon

Standard 60 £50

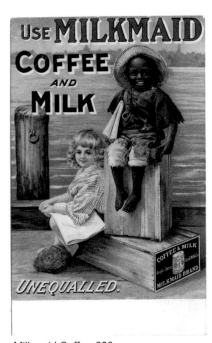

Milkmaid Coffee £30

Remington Typewriters	
Poster type	£20
Ridgway's	
Tea Estate scenes	£3
Rowntree	
Louis Wain Cats	£75
Rowntree's Postcard Series	£2
St. Bartholomew's Hospital	
Reconstuction Appeal	£1
St.Ivel	
GB views/Set 12	£1.50
St. Paul's Hospital/Set 12	
£1,000 Competition	£1
Sainsbury's Margarine	
Crelos/Early Days of Sport	£15
/Fairy Tales	£15
Selfridge Co.	£3
Shippam's	
Food production scenes	£5
Shops/Stores	
Artist sketches	£5
Photographic/Printed	£15
Shurey's Publications	
Twopenny Tube/Set 12	£6
Various subjects	£1.50
Singer Sewing Machines	
Sewing Machines Worldwide	£10
Aviation studies	£6
Battleships	£3
Sketchy Bits	
Various subjects	£1.50
Smart Novels	
Dance Band Leaders/Set 10	£6
Greetings/Coloured	£1.50
Various subjects	£1.50
Spillers	£12
Sportex Cloth	
Dog studies	£8
Spratt's Dog Foods	
Dog studies	£8
Sutton & Sons	
Flowers/Vegetables	£1.50
Swan Fountain Pens	
Comic sketches	£6
Symond's London Stores	
Comic sketches	£8
T.A.T.	
The `Months' Series	£4
Other subjects	£1.50
Thomson D.C.	
Various subjects	£1.50

Thorley
Cattle photographs £6

Time Magazine
Subscription cards .75

Tiny Tots
Greetings/Coloured £8

Tit-Bits
Poster type £6

Tower Tea
Proverb Series £10

Trent Pottery
Trent Bridge Publishing Co. £6

Tussauds Madame
Tableaux/Set 12/Tuck R. & Sons £3

Two Steeples Hosiery
Hunting sketches £3

Typhoo Tea
Various subjects/Oilette £3

Underwood Typewriters
Poster type £20

Van Houten's Cocoa
MGM Film Stars £5
Colouring Cards of Birds/
Set of 6 in Folder/Price per card £4
Dutch scenes £2
Art Sketches/Uncaptioned £1.50

Virol
Children of all Nations £6

Vitality
Physical Culture studies £6

Ward Lock
Naval photographs £3

Weekly Tale-Teller
Various subjects £1.50

Weekly Telegraph
Tom Browne sketches £8

Weldon's Bazaar
KE VII Coronation Souvenir £10

White Horse Whisky
Maggs Coaching studies £2

Wood-Milne Rubber Heel
Glamour studies/Sager £15
GB views £1.50

Wrench
Insurance cards £8

Yes or No
Various subjects £1.50

Ackerman Wine advert £35

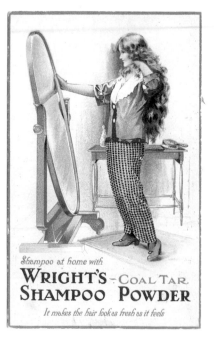

Wrights Shampoo £20

Main Gas Cooker £38

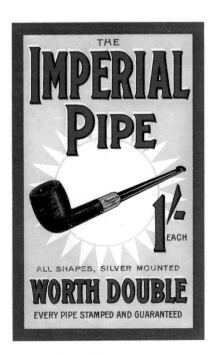

Imperial Pipe £40

REWARD CARDS
Given away for good school work and atten-dance etc.

COMPANIES
Cadbury Bros.
Birds/Set 25	£6
Birds and their Eggs/Set 12	£6
Butterflies/Set 32	£8
Map Cards	£8

Ficolax
Fruit sketches	£4

Milkmaid Condensed Milk
Royalty sketches	£8

Nectar Tea
Bird sketches	£6
Tea Estate sketches	£4

Reckitt
Naval History	£6

Scott's Emulsion £5

EDUCATION AUTHORITIES
Barking Education Committee
Homeland Series/Court Size	£6

County Borough of West Ham
Court Size	£6

Erith Education Committee
Tuck R. & Sons/Castles etc.	£3

Hampshire County Council
GB views	£1.50

Huddersfield Education Committee
GB views	£3

Isle of Ely Education Committee
Nature Notes	£3

Leyton School Board/Pre-1902
Various sizes and series	£4

London County Council
Battleships/6 x 4 size/ S. Cribb	£5
Various Subjects	£1.50

Oxfordshire Education Committee
British Wild Flowers	£3

Reading EducationCommittee
Animals/Historical	£3

School Board for London
Various subjects/Pre-1895	£5
Various subjects/1895-1902	£3

Surrey Education Committee
GB views	£1.50

Walthamstow Education Committee
Paintings/Views	£3

Wanstead School Board
Flowers	£4

ANIMALS

If postcard collecting was originally the province of the young girls of the Edwardian age, then it is to them and their interest in this subject, that we owe the great legacy of Animal cards bequeathed us. Always an attractive collecting area, then as now. Animal cards were produced in considerable quantity, with almost every type of bird or beast depicted somewhere. Today's collectors tend to prefer Artist-drawn cards, rather than the photographic studies.

Market Report
Better artist drawn cat cards will always find appreciative owners but not photographic studies. Dogs are a little quiet at the moment. There are still visitors to the zoo sections and taxidermy has its followers.

ANTHROPORMORPHIC
(Animals in human dress)

Chromo-Litho	£10
Photographic/Printed	£3

BIRDS

NVP Sluis Birdfood	£1.50
Racing Pigeons	£5
Scilly Isles/C.J. King	£1
Art Studies	£2
Photographic Studies	£1

Tuck R. & Sons

British Birds & their Eggs/ Aquarette Series 9218/9399/9519	£6

BUTTERFLIES

Art Studies	£3
Photographic Studies	£1

Tuck R. & Sons

Butterflies	£6
British Butterflies and Moths	£6
Butterflies on the Wing	£6
Educational Series No. 8/Set 6	£8

CATTLE

Miscellaneous Studies	£1.50

CATS

Chromo-Litho	£12
Mainzer, Alfred/Post-war	£2
Art Studies	£3
Photographic Studies	£1.50
Inter Art	£5

DOGS

Military Dogs/WW1	£6
Spratt's Dog Foods	£8
Art Studies	£3+
Photographic Studies	£2

Dog Carts

Belgian	£3
French Milk Carts	£25+
French other Carts	£25+
Swiss	£5
Other European types	£5

Within these prices, named breeds would be worth more than un-named.

DONKEYS

Donkey Carts/RP	£6
Seaside	£2
Domestic	£2

FISH

Art Studies	£3
Photographic Studies	£1.50

Chromo Litho £12

Dogs, Royal Navy by Herbert Ward £5

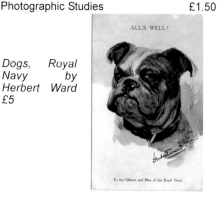

Tuck Oillette, Hilda Walker £4

HORSES

Horses and Carts	£6
Ponies and Traps	£4
Working Horses	£3
Art Studies	£4
Photographic Studies	£2

Coaching

Vanderbilt Coach	£12
Holiday types	£3
State/Ceremonial Coaches	£1.50
Old Coaching Inns of England/	
Set 16/J.C. Maggs	£2

PIGS

Early/Chromo-Litho	£15
Farmyard scenes	£2
Art Studies	£5
Photographic Studies	£3

POULTRY

Easter Chicks	£1.50
Art Studies	£4
Photographic Studies	£1.50

Tuck R. & Sons

Prize Poultry/Oilette	£6

TAXIDERMY

Booth Museum/Brighton	£2
Bramber Museum	£1.50
Stuffed Animals/Fish	£3

WILD ANIMALS

Frogs	£3
Rabbits	£3
Art studies	£3
Photographic Studies	£1

Tuck R. & Sons

Wild Animals/Oilette	£3

ZOO ANIMALS

Art Studies	£3
Photographic Studies	£2

Official Issues

London Zoo/Whipsnade	£2

Series

Zoological Society of London/	
H.A.J. Schultz & Co.	£5

Zoological Society, London   £5

Art Study, £4

SERIES
Tuck R. & Sons

Educational Series	£9

WELFARE SOCIETIES

Abattoir scenes/U.S.A.	£8
Anti-Bloodsports	£12
Anti-Vivisection	£12
Cat Protection Organisations	£10
National Canine Defence League	£10
Our Dumb Friends League	£10
R.S.P.C.A./R.S.P.B.	£10
Vegetarian Society	£10
Veterinary Services	£12

ARTISTS

This is a select index of better known artists who designed for the picture postcard in both Subject and Topographical fields. It is not comprehensive, as many thousands of artists world-wide have contributed to the medium during the past century. The price stated may be taken as a guide to the most typical and representative work of the artist concerned, although in the Subject field, this price may be qualified by the theme depicted. With all artists so much depends upon the individual card, the design, the period, the publisher and of course the con-dition. I have done nothing more than indicate the general price area into which the artist falls, but certain rare cards by particular artists may dramatically exceed this figure. The great majority of artists listed below are either British, or have produced cards which are collected in this country. There are some excellent catalogues available which list the artists of France, Italy, Russia, USA etc. but I do not consider it practical to copy out several thousand names which would have little relevance to the British market. We have intoduced more new artists to the section and illustrations, which we hope will help.

Market Report
There are plenty of buying opportunities in this section as many artists have few, if any, seri-ous followers. On the domestic front, early Attwells, Tom Browne and AR Quinton are attracting most interest.

M.A.	Comic	£1		**Anichini, Ezio**	Art Deco	£15
S.A.	Comic	£1.50		**Aranda, Pilar**	Art Deco	£8
T.A.	Comic	£1.50		**Ardizonne, E**	General	£3
Abeille, Jack	Art Nouveau	£60		**Aris, Ernest**	Comic	£3
	Glamour	£50			General	£1.50
Acker, Flori Von	General	£1		**Armitage, A.F.**	General	£1.50
Ackroyd, W.M.	Animals	£3		**Asti, Angelo**	Glamour	£6
Adams, C.J.	General	£1				
Adams, Frank	General	£3				
Adams, J.T.	General	£1.50				
Adams, M	General	£1				
Adams, Will	Comic	£1.50				
Addison, W.G.	General	£1.50				
Ainsley, Anne	Animals	£3				
Albertini	Glamour	£6				
Aldin, Cecil	Animals	£6				
Allan, A	General	£1				
Allen, S.J.	General	£1				
Allen, W.	General	£1.50				
Alys, M	Children	£1.50				
Ambler, C	Animals	£3				
Anders, O	Animals	£6				
	Comic	£3				
Anderson, Alan	Railway	£3				
Anderson, Anne	Children	£6				
Anderson, V.C.	Children	£4				
Andrews, E	General	£1.50				
Andrews, ET	Early	£10				

Angelo Asti £6

Attwell, Mabel Lucie	Children/	
	Pre-1918	£12
	1918-1939	£8
	1940 on	£5
	Modern Repros	.50
Atche	Glamour	£30
Austen, Alex	General	£1
Austerlitz, E	Comic	£3
Austin E.H.S. Barnes	Animals	£12
Austin, Winifred	Animals	£4
Aveline,F	Glamour	£6
Aveling, S.	General	£1.50
Azzoni, N.	Children	£4
H.S.B.	Comic	£1.50
J.O.B.	Comic	£2
Baertson	Military	£4
Bady, Carlos	Glamour	£5
Bailey G.O.	Glamour	£4
Bairnsfather, Bruce	Comic	£4
	Theatre	£30
Baker, G.	Military	£4
Baker, H Granville	Military	£6
Bakst, Leon	Art Deco	£50
Balestrieri, L	Glamour	£8
	General	£4
Ball, Wilfred	General	£2
Bamber, George A	Comic	£2
Baness	General	£1
Bannister, A.F.D.	Aviation	£4
	Shipping	£4
Bantock	Art Deco	£8
Barbara, S	Art Nouveau	£25
Barber, Court	Glamour	£7
Barber, C.W.	Children	£3
	Glamour	£3
Barde	Flowers	£1.50
Barham, S	Children	£8
Barker, Cecily M	Children	£12
Barnes,A.E.	Animals	£20
Barnes, G.L.	Animals	£15
	Comic	£8
Barraud, A	General	£1.50
Barraud, N	Animals	£5
Barrett, A	Military	£3
Barribal, W	Children	£12
	Glamour	£12
	Theatre	£25

FOND MEMORIES.

W. Barribal £12

Barthel, Paul	General	£1.50
Bartoli, Guiseppi	General	£5
Basch, Arpad	Art Nouveau	£110
Bask, W	General	£1
Bateman, H.M.	Comic	£8
Bates, Leo	Glamour	£5
Bates, Marjorie C.	Literary	£5
	General	£3
Baumgarten, Fritz	Children	£4
Bayer, R.W.	Flowers	£1.50
Beale, Sophia	General	£2
Beards, Harold	Comic	£1.50
Bebb, Rosa	Animals	£6
	General	£1.50
Becker, C.	Military	£8
	Sport	£8
Bee	Comic	£1
Beecroft, Herbert	General	£4
Beer, Andrew	General	£1.50
Beerts, Albert	Military	£5
Belcher, George	Comic	£4
Belet, A	Pierrotts	£8
Benois, Alexander	Various	£25

Beraud, N	Animals	£4
	Military	£5
Berkeley, Edith	General	£1
Berkeley, Stanley	Animals	£3
Berthon, Paul	Art Nouveau	£80
Bertiglia, A	Children	£8
Bianchi	Glamour	£4
Biggar, J.L.	Comic	£2
Bilibin, Ivan	Art Nouveau	£55
Billing, M	General	£1.50
Billinge, Ophelia	Animals	£5
Birch, Nora-Annie	Children	£4
Bird, H	Sport	£5
Birger	Art Deco	£20
Birtles, H.	General	£1.50
Black, Algernon	Shipping	£8
Black, Montague B.	Shipping	£8
Black, W. Milne	Comic	£3
Blair, Andrew	General	£1.50
Blair, John	General	£1.50
Bob	Comic	£2
	General	£1.50
Boccasile, Gino	Art Deco	£45
Boecker, A.G.	Flowers	£1.50
Bohrdt, Hans	Shipping	£20

Hans Bohrdt £20

See feature on Pages 136-137

Boileau, Philip	Glamour	£10
Bolton, F.N.	General	£1
Bompard, S	Glamour	£6
Boriss, Margret	Children	£6
Borrow, W.H.	General	£2
Bothams, W	General	£1
Bottaro, E	Glamour	£10

Bottomley, Edwin	Animals	£3
Bottomley, George	Glamour	£3
Boulanger, Maurice	Animals	£10
	Comic	£10
Bouret, Germaine Bourillon	Children	£6
	Military	£5
Boutet, Henri	Art Nouveau	£35
Bowden, Doris	Children	£6
Bowers, Albert	General	£2
Bowers, Stephen	General	£2
Bowley, A.L.	Children	£12
Bowley M.	Animals	£6
Boyne, T	General	£1
Bradshaw, Percy V	Comic	£6
	Political	£8
Braun, W	Glamour	£6
Breanski, Arthur de	General	£2
Brett, Molly	Children	£3
Bridgeman, Arthur W	General	£2
Brisley, Nina	Children	£5
Broadrick, Jack	Comic	£2
Brown, Maynard	Glamour	£4
Browne, Stewart Browne, Tom	Theatre	£15
	Adv/Inserts	£10
	Adv/Literary	£10
	Posters	£15/£75
	Cathedrals	£6
	Comic	£4
	Theatre	£20
Brundage, Frances	Children/ Chromo-Litho	£15
	Others	£6
	General	£4
Brunelleschi, U	Art Deco	£100
Buchanan, Fred	Comic	£3
Buchel, Charles	Theatre	£18
Budge	Comic	£1
Bull, Rene	Comic	£4
Burger, R	General	£1
Burgess, Arthur	Shipping	£8
Burnard, Victor W.	General	£1.50
Burton, F.W.	General	£1.50
Bushby, Thomas	General	£3
Busi, Adolfo	Art Deco	£12
	Glamour	£6
Bussiere, G	Art Nouveau	£30

Gozzard, J.W.	General	£1.50
Graeff	Comic	£2
Graf, Marte	Art Deco	£10
Grant, Carleton	General	£1
Grasset, Eugene	Art Nouveau	£75
Green, Alec E.	Children	£3
Green, Roland	Animals	£3
Greenall, Jack	Comic	£2
Greenaway, Kate	Children/	
	1903 printing	£65
	later printing	£15
Greenbank, A.	Glamour	£8
Greiner, M	Children	£10
Gresley, A.	Flowers	£1.50
Gretty, G	General	£1.50
Grey, Mollie	Children	£2
Gribble, Bernard F.	General	£2
Grimes	Comic	£3
Grin, C.U.	Comic	£1.50
Grosze, Manni	Art Deco	£10
Grunewald	Art Deco	£10
Guerzoni, C	Glamour	£8
Guggenberger, T	General	£4
Guillaume A.	Art Nouveau	£75
	Comic	£5
Gunn, A.	Glamour	£5
Gunn Gwennet	Comic	£2
Gurnsey, C.	Comic	£1.50
Guy, T.	General	£1
E.A.H.	Comic	£1.50
F.W.H.	Comic	£3
S.H.	Comic	£1
Hager, Nini	Art Nouveau	£80
Hailey, Edward	General	£1
Haller, A.	Flowers	£2
Halliday	Comic	£3
Hamilton, E	Shipping	£8
Hamilton, J.M.	Sport	£18
Hamish	Comic	£2
Hammick, J.W.	Glamour	£3
Hammond, J.	Flowers	£1.50
Hampel, Walter	Art Nouveau	£85
Hanbury, F. Schmidt	General	£1.50
Hannaford	General	£1.50

Hansi	Children	£15
	Political	£15
Harbour, Jennie	Art Deco	£15
Hardy, Dudley	Comic	£6
	Glamour	£9
	Political	£12
	Shipping	£20
	Theatre	£20
Hardy, Florence	Children	£6
Hardy, F.	Art Deco	£10
Hardy, F.C.	Military	£4
Harriet	Comic	£1
Harrison, E. Florence	Glamour	£6
Hart, Josef	Art Nouveau	£35

Josef Hart, Art Nouveau £35

Hartridge, Norman	Children	£10
Harvey, F.	Comic	£1.50
Haslehust, E.W.	General	£1.50
Hassall, John	Comic	£5
	Court Size	£15
	Theatre	£30
	General	£4
Hauby, S.	Art Nouveau	£12
Haviland, Frank	Glamour	£5
Hayes, F.W.	General	£1.50
Hayes, Sydney	Animals	£1.50

Hebblethwaite, S.H.	Comic	£3
Heinirch	General	£6
Henckel, Carl	Military	£6
Henley	Comic	£1.50
Henley, W.C.	General	£1.50
Henry, Thomas	Children	£6
	Comic	£6
Herouard	Glamour	£15
Herrfurth, Oskar	Children	£10
Heusser, Harry	Shipping	£8
Hey, Paul	General	£4
Heyermanns,S.	General	£1.50
Heyermans, John A	General	£1.50
Hickling, P.B.	General	£1.50
Hier, Prof. van	General	£1.50
Higham, Sydney	General	£1.50
Hiles, Bartram	General	£2
Hill, L. Raven	Political	£5
Hilton, Alf	Comic	£2
Hines, B.	General	£1..50
Hodgson, W. Scott	General	£1
Hofer, Andre	Glamour	£7
Hoffman, H.W.	General	£1
Hoffman, J.	Art Nouveau	£90
Hoffmann, Anton	Military	£8
Hohenstein, A	Art Nouveau	£35
Hohlwein, Ludwig	Advertising	£25
	Military	£10

Holloway, Edgar A.	Military	£12
Hollyer, Eva	Children	£8
Home, Gordon	General	£1.50
Hood, Eileen	Animals	£4
Hopcroft, G.E.	General	£1.50
Hopking, Noel	Animals	£1
Horder, Margaret	Children	£2
Horrell, Charles	Glamour	£4
Horsfall, Mary	Children	£6
	Glamour	£4
Horwitz, Helena	Glamour	£4
Howard, C.T.	General	£1.50
Howard, Jim	Comic	£1.50
Howell, E.	Comic	£1.50
Hudson, Gerald	Military	£4
Hughes, Alun	Comic	£1.50
Hughes, Lloyd	Comic	£1.50
Hughes, R.	General	£1
Hummel	Children	£4
Hunt, Edgar	Animals	£2
Hunt, Muriel	Animals	£4
Hunter, Mildred C	Animals	£4
Hurst, Hal	Comic	£3
Hutchinson, F.	General	£1
Hyde, Graham	Comic	£6
Ibbetson, Ernest	Comic	£6
	Military	£12
Icart, Louis	Glamour	£12
Innes, John	General	£2
Inskip, J. Henry	General	£1.50
Iranez, J	Children	£4
Ironico	Comic	£1.50
Irwin	Comic	£1
J.R.J.	Comic	£1.50
Jackson, Helen	Children	£18
Jackson, Ian	Glamour	£5
Jacobs, Helen	Children	£8
Jafuri, R.	General	£3
James, Frank	Animals	£1.50
James, Ivy Millicent	Children	£10
Jank, Angelo	Art Nouveau	£35
Jarach, A	Glamour	£12
Jay, Cecil	Glamour	£5

Mary Horsfall, Glamour £4

Ivy Millicent James (IMJ) Children £10

Jenkins, G.H.	General	£1.50
Jester	Comic	£1.50
Jo	Comic	£1
Johnson, M.	General	£1.50
Johnson, S.	General	£1.50
Jossot	Art Nouveau	£160
Josza, Carl	Art Nouveau	£60
Jotter	Comic Types	£3
	Greetings	£2
	Hotels	£3/10
	Derbys/Cornwall	£1
	Sheffield/Ireland	£4
	Views -Other	£2
Jung, Maurice	Art Nouveau	£500
A.H.K.	General	£1
C.K.	Comic	£1.50
E.M.T.K.	Comic	£1.50
Kaby	Glamour	£4
Kainradl, L	Art Nouveau	£100
Kammerer, Rob	General	£1.50
Karaktus	Comic	£1.50
Kaskeline, Fred	Children	£6
Katinka	Art Deco	£12
Kaufmann, J.C.	Animals	£2
Keene, Elmer	General	£1.50
Keene, Frank	Comic	£1.50
Keene, Minnie	Animals	£2
Keesey, Walter M.	General	£1
Kempe	Children	£6
Kennedy, A.E.	Animals	£6
	Comic	£6
	Theatre	£12
Kerr, Tom	Children	£1
Kid	Comic	£1.50

Kidd, Will	Children	£6
Kieszkow	Art Nouveau	£30
Kimball, Alonzo	Glamour	£5
King A. Price	General	£1.50
King, Edward	General	£3
King, Gunning	General	£3
King, Jessie M.	Art Nouveau	£85
King, W.B.	Comic	£1.50
King, Yeend	General	£1.50
Kinnear, J.	General	£2
Kinsella, E.P.	Children	£6
	Comic	£6
	Theatre	£20
Kircher, A.	Naval	£4
Kirchner, Raphael		
/Early	Art Nouveau	£80
/WW1 period	Glamour	£30
/Bruton Galleries	Glamour	£25
Kirk, A.H.	General	£1.50
Kirkbach	Children	£3
Kirkpatrick	General	£1
Kirmse, Persis	Animals	£5
Klein, Christina	General/	
	Chromo-Litho	£6
	Later Issues	£3
Kley, Paul	Chromo-Litho	£6
	Other printings	£2
Klodic	Shipping	£6
Knox, W	General	£1.50
Koch, Ludwig	Sport	£6
Koehler, Mela	Art Deco	£70
	Art Nouveau	£120
Koehler Mela Broman	Art Deco	£25
Kokoschka	Art Nouveau	£600
Konopa	Art Nouveau	£35
Kosa	Art Nouveau	£100
Koy	Comic	£1.50
Kulas, J.V.	Art Nouveau	£35
Kupka	Art Nouveau	£75
Kyd	Comic	£8
	Literary	£12
	London Life	£10
Lacy, Chas J.de	Shipping	£12
Lajoux, Edmond	Military	£5
Lamb, Eric	General	£1
Lambert, H.G.C. Marsh	Children	£5

Lancere, Yergenyi	General	£15
Lang, W.	Art Nouveau	£35
Larcombe, Ethel	Art Nouveau	£35
Lasalle, Jean	Glamour	£2
	General	£2
Laskoff F	Art Nouveau	£50
Lauder, C.J.	General	£1.50
Lautrec, H. de Toulouse	Art Nouveau	£600
Lawes, H.	General	£1
Laz	Comic	£1.50
Leete, Alfred	Comic	£4
Leggatt, C.P.	Comic	£2
Lehmann, Felix	Sport	£6
Lehmann, Phil	Comic	£2
Leigh, Conrad	Military	£4
Lelee Leopold	Art Nouveau	£60
LeMunyon, Pearl Fidler	Glamour	£6
Leng, Max	Art Nouveau	£30
Leodud Di	Art Deco	£6
Leonnec, G.	Glamour	£15
Leroux Pierre Albert	Military	£5
Leroy	Military	£5
Lesker, H.	Art Deco	£8
Lessieux, E. Louis	Art Nouveau	£40
	Shipping	£25
Lester, Adrienne	Animals	£3
Lester, Ralph	Glamour	£3
Lewin, F.G.	Children	£6
	Comic	£4
Lilien, E.M.	Art Nouveau	£40
	General	£8
Lime, H.	Comic	£1
Lindsay, J.	General	£1
Lindsell, L.	Glamour	£3
Livemont, Privat	Art Nouveau	£100
Lloyd, T. Ivester	Glamour	£4
	Military	£5
Loffler Berthold	Art Nouveau	£100
Loffler, Lovat	Art Nouveau	£30
Loir Luigi	General	£6
Long, L.M.	General	£1.50
Longley, Chilton	Art Deco	£35

Longmire, R.O.	Political	£10
Longstaffe, Ernest	General	£1.50
Loreley	Art Deco	£15
Lorenz, Fablus	Glamour	£10
Love, H. Montagu	Military	£6
	General	£2
Lovering, I.	General	£1.50
Lowe, Meta	Children	£2
Luckcott G.Y.	Comic	£1.50
Ludgate	Comic	£2
Ludlow, Hal	Comic	£2
Ludovici, A.	Children	£5
	Comic	£3
	Political	£3
Luke W.	Comic	£2
Lumley, Savile	Military	£4
Lynen, Amedee	General	£4
C.M.	Comic	£1
M.S.M.	Glamour	£15
P.C.M.	Comic	£1.50
Mac/National Series	Comic	£2
Mac	Animals	£5
	Comic	£3
MacBean L.C.	Comic	£2
McGill, Donald	Comic/	
	Early Dated	£8
	Pre-1914	£5
	1914-1939	£3
	`New'	£1

I'M LIVING ON THE FAT OF THE LAND AT BRIGHTON

Donald McGill, Comic £3

McIntyre, J.	General	£1.50
McIntyre, R.F.	General	£1.50
McNeill, J.	Military	£12

Macdonald, A.K.	Art Nouveau	£35
Mackain, F.	Comic	£3
Macleod, F.	Comic	£2
Macpherson, John	General	£1
MacWhirter, J.	General	£1.50
Maggs, J.C.	Coaching	£2
Maguire, Bertha	General	£1.50
Maguire, Helena	Animals	£8
	General	£3
Mailick, A.	Glamour	£4
	General	£3
Mainzer, Alfred	Animals	£3
Mair, H. Willebeek le	Children	£8

H. Willebeek le Mair, Children £8

Mallet, Beatrice	Children	£5
Mallet, Dennis	Comic	£1.50
Manavian, V.	Comic	£2
Mann, James S	Shipping	£12
Marchant, Leslie P.	Comic	£1.50
Marco, M.	Glamour	£3
Marechaux, C.	Glamour	£4
Margetson, Hester	Children	£8
Marisch, G.	Art Nouveau	£75
Maroc	Comic	£1
Marshall, Alice	Children	£12
Mart	Comic	£1.50
Martin, L.B.	Comic	£3
	Children	£5
Martin, Phil	Comic	£2
Martineau, Alice	Glamour	£8
	General	£3
	Children	£8

Martini, A.	Adverts	£35
	Political	£25
Martino R. de	General	£1
Marty, Andre	Art Deco	£15
Mason, Finch	Comic/Sport	£4
Mason, Frank H.	Shipping	£5
Mason, George W	Comic	£4
Mastroianni, D.	General	£2
Mataloni, G.	Art Nouveau	£30
Matthison, W.	General	£1.50
Maurice, Reg	Comic	£2
Mauzan, A.	Children	£6
	Glamour	£10
	Political	£6
	Art Deco	£20
	General	£3
May, F.S.	Comic	£2
May, J.A.	Comic	£2
May, Phil	Comic/	
	Write-away	£8
	Oilette	£4

Phil May, Comic £8

Maybank, Thomas	Children	£12
Mayer, Lou	Glamour	£5
Meadows, Chas	Comic	£2
Menpes, Mortimer	Children	£3

Meras, Rene	Glamour	£7	**Morgan, F.E.**	Comic	£3
Mercer, Joyce	Art Deco	£25	**Morris, M.**	General	£1.50
	Children	£25	**Morrow, Albert**	Theatre	£12
Meredith, Jack	Comic	£2	**Moser, Koloman**	Art Nouveau	£120
Merte, O.	Animals	£5	**Mostyn, Dorothy**	Glamour	£4
Meschini, G.	Art Deco	£35	**Mostyn, Marjorie**	Glamour	£4
Metlicovitz, L.	Art Nouveau	£35	**Mouton, G.**	Glamour	£10
Meunier, Henri	Art Nouveau	£95	**Mucha, Alphonse**	Art Nouveau	£100+
Meunier, Suzanne	Glamour	£20		Exhibition	£100
Mich	Comic	£1.50		Slav Period	£50

Mignot, Victor	Art Nouveau	£35
Mike	Comic	£1
Miller, Hilda T.	Children/ Liberty	£15
	Other Pubs.	£8
Milliere, Maurice	Glamour	£15
Millor	Flowers	£1
Millot	Greetings	£1
Mills, Ernest, H.	Animals	£4
Monestier, C.	Glamour	£5

Alphonse Mucha, Art Nouveau £125

Monier, Maggy	Glamour	£10
Moore, A. Winter	General	£1.50
Moore, F.	Railway	£3
Montague, Love, H	Military	£8
Montague, R.	Shipping	£6
	General	£1.50
Montedoro, M	Art Deco	£50
Moreland, Arthur	Comic	£3
	Political	£5

Muggiai	Glamour	£15
Mulholland, S.A.	General	£1
Muller, A.	Animals	£4
Muller, Valery	General	£8
Muraton, E.	Flowers	£2
Murhaghan Kathleen, I.	Children	£4
Mutter, K.	General	£4
Naillod, C.S.	Glamour	£6
Nam, Jacques	Glamour	£10
Nanni,G.	Glamour	£6
Nap	Comic	£2
Nash, A.A.	Children	£4
Nerman	Art Deco	£18
	Theatre	£25
Neumont, M	Glamour	£5
Neville-Cumming, R	Shipping	£8
Newton, G.E.	General	£1.50
Ney	Glamour	£10
Nicholson, J	Shipping	£5
Nielsen, Harry B.	Comic	£2
Nielsen, Vivienne	Animals	£3
Nixon, K.	Children	£10
Noble, Ernest	Comic	£3

'David Copperfield from his Aunt, Miss Betsey Trotwood.
"I was on the point of slinking off when there came out of the house a lady with her handkerchief tied over her cap, and a pair of gardening gloves on her hands. ___ I knew her immediately to be Miss Betsey." *David Copperfield Chap.XIII*

Giovanni Nanni £6

Norfield, Edgar	Comic	£1.50
Norman, Parsons	General	£1.50
Norman, Val	General	£1.50
Norwood, A.Harding	General	£1.50
Noury, Gaston	Art Nouveau	£80
Nystrom, Jenny	Children	£12
	Glamour	£12
O'Beirne, F.	Military	£12
O'Kay	Comic	£1
O'Neill, Rose	Children	£8
Operti, A.	General	£5
Opper, F.	Comic	£1.50
Orens, Denizard	Political	£18
Ost. A.	Art Nouveau	£30
Ostrumova-Lebeva,A	General	£25
Outcault, R.F.	Children	£8
	Comic	£5
Outhwaite, Ida R.	Children	£25
Overell, J.	Children	£4
Overnell	Children	£5
Owen, Will	Comic	£4
	Theatre	£12
Oyston, George	General	£1.50
Paget, Wal	General	£1.50
Palmer, Phyllis, M.	Children	£5
Palmer, Sutton	General	£1.50

Pannett, R.	Glamour	£8
	Theatre	£18
Parker, N.	Animals	£4
Parkinson, Ethel	Children	£5
Parlett, Harry	Comic	£1.50
Parlett, T.	Comic	£2
Parr, B.F.C.	General	£1
Parr, Doreen	Children	£4

Doreen Parr, Children £4

Partridge, Bernard	Political	£4
Parsons, F.J.	Railway	£3
Patek, August	Art Nouveau	£12
Patella, B.	Art Nouveau	£35
Paterson, Vera	Children	£3
Paulus	Military	£3
Payne, Arthur C	General	£2
Payne, G.M.	Comic	£3
	Glamour	£3
Payne, Harry		
/Tuck Early	Horses	£40
/Tuck Early	Military	£40
/Metropolitan Police	General	£40
/Wild West	General	£30
/Coaching	Animals	£30
/Gale & Polden	Military	£15
/Stewart & Woolf	Military	£15
/Badges & Wearers	Military	£12+
/Oilettes	Horses	£6
/Oilettes	Military	£6+
/Military in London	Military	£4
/Rural Life	General	£5
/Other	General	£10+
Pears, Chas	Advertising	£15

Pearse, Susan B	Children	£12
Peddie, Tom	Glamour	£3
Pellegrini, E.	Glamour	£18
Peltier, L.	Glamour	£8
Penley, Edwin A.	General	£1.50
Pennington, Oswald	Shipping	£7
Penny, Theo	Comic	£1.50
Penot, A.	Glamour	£15
Pepin, Maurice	Glamour	£12
Peras	Glamour	£8
Percival, E.D.	General	£1.50
Perlberg, F.	Animals	£4
	General	£1
Perly	Comic	£1.50
Person, Alice Fidler	Glamour	£6
Petal	Comic	£1
Peterson, Hannes	General	£2
Pfaff, C.	General	£6
Philippi, Robert	Art Nouveau	£15
Phillimore, R.P.	General	£3
Phipson, E.A.	General	£1.50
Phiz	Dickens	£5
Pike, Sidney	General	£1.50
Pillard,	Glamour	£6
	Military	£6
Pinder, Douglas	General	£1
Pingers	Political	£6
Pinhey, Edith	General	£1
Pinkawa, Anton	Art Nouveau	£30
Piper, George	Children	£3
Pirkis	Comic	£3
Pitcher, Henrie	General	£3
Pizer, Herbert	Glamour	£8
Plumstead, Joyce	Children	£8
Polzin, G.	General	£4
Pope, Dorothy T.	Animals	£8
Popini	Art Nouveau	£30
	Glamour	£5
Poulbot, Francisque	Children	£4
Poy	Comic	£1.50
Praga, Alfred	Shipping	£12
Presland, A.L.	Flowers	£1.50
Preston, Chloe	Children	£9

Prosnocimi, A.	General	£1.50
Purser, Phyllis	Children	£4
Pyp	Comic	£2
Quatremain, W.W.	General	£1.50
Quinnell, Cecil W.	Glamour	£4
	Literary	£4
Quinton, A.R.		
/Salmon J. & Co.	South Africa	£12+
	Ostende	£10+
	General	£3+
	1960/70 Period	.75
	Reprints/7 digit	
	computer nos.	.25
/Tuck R. & Sons	General	£4+

A.R. Quinton £3

Quinton, F.E.	General	£1.50
Quinton, Harry	Comic	£2
Quips	Comic	£1.50
A.F.R.	Comic	£1.50
F.A.R.	General	£1.50
J.S.R.	Comic	£1.50
Rackham, Arthur	Children	£25
Raemaekers, Louis	Political	£3
Ralph, Lester	Glamour	£6
Raimondi, R.	General	£3
Rambler	General	£1
Ramsey, George S.	General	£1
Rankin, George	Animals	£3
Rappini	Glamour	£5
	General	£4
Ratcliffe, W.W.	General	£4
Rauh, Ludwig	Glamour	£15
Raven, Phil.	Comic	£1.50
Read, F.W.	Glamour	£3
	General	£1

Read, T. Buchanan	General	£1
Reckling, L.G.	General	£1
Reichert, C.	Animals	£4
Reiss, Fritz	General	£5
Remington Frederick	General	£8
Renaud, M.	Flowers	£1
Renault, A.	Flowers	£1
Rennie, M.	General	£1.50
Rex	Comic	£1
Reynolds, Frank	Comic	£4
	Literary	£5
Ribas	Glamour	£10
Richardson, Agnes	Children	£5
Richardson, Charles	Comic	£1.50
Richardson, R.V.	Comic	£2
Richardson, R.W.E.	General	£1.50
Richmond, Leonard	Railways	£10
Rickard, J.	Children	£8
Right	Comic	£2
Riley, W.E.	Military	£3
Ritchie, Alick P.F.	Comic	£3
Ritter, Paul	General	£4
Robert, Lucien	Glamour	£15

Roberts, Howard L.	Comic	£2
Roberts, Violet M	Animals	£20
	Comic	£20
Robida, A.	General	£6
Robinson, W. Heath	Comic	£6
Rodella, G.	Glamour	£5
Rog	Comic	£1.50
Romney, George	Railways	£3
Rooke, H.K.	Shipping	£10
Rose, Freda Mabel	Children	£3
Rosenvinge, Odin	Shipping	£12
Rossi, J.C.	Art Nouveau	£65
Rostro	Political	£15
Rousse, Frank	General	£2
Rowland, Ralph	Comic	£2
Rowlandson, G.D.	Military	£5
	Comic	£3
	General	£1.50
	Sports series	£12

G.D.Rowlandson Sports cards £12

Rowntree, Harry	Animals	£12
	Comic	£12
Rust, A.	Comic	£1.50
Ryan, F.	Comic	£1.50
Ryland, Henry	Glamour	£8
Rylander	Art Deco	£15
S. (Capital)	Comic	£1.50
S. (Script)	Comic	£1.50
J.M.S.	Comic	£1.50
K.S.	Comic	£1.50
M.S.	Children	£1.50
S.E.S.	Comic	£1.50
Sachetti, E.	Political	£8
Sager, Xavier	Glamour	£15

Lucien Robert £15

Salaman, Edith	General	£5
Salmony, G.	Glamour	£5
Samokiche, N	Military	£15
Sancha, F.	Political	£8
Sand, Adina	Glamour	£54
Sanders, A.E.	General	£1.50
Sanderson, Amy	Children	£3
Sandford, H.Dix	Children	£6
	Comic/Coons	£8
Sandy-Hook	Shipping	£12
Sarg, Tony	Comic	£2
Sartoi, E.	General	£1
Sauber	General	£6
	Social History	£6
Saville Rena	Children	£1.50
Sayer, Henry	Comic	£5
Schiele, Egon	Art Nouveau	£100+
Schiesl, R.	General	£3
Schmidt-Hamburg	Shipping	£10
	General	£1.50
Schonflug, Fritz	Comic	£4
Schonian	Animals	£4
Schubert, H.	Glamour	£5
Schweiger, L.	General	£4
Scottie	Glamour	£6
Scribbler	Comic	£1.50
Scrivener, Maude	Animals	£3
Severn, Walter	General	£1.50
Sgrilli	Children	£5
Shand, C.E.	Art Deco	£10
Shaw, H.G.	Animals	£6
Shaw, W. Stocker	Comic	£2
Shelton, S.	General	£1.50
Shepheard, G.E.	Comic	£5
Sherrin, A.	General	£1.50
Sherwin, D.	General	£1
Shmerling, Oscar	General	£7
Shoesmith, Kenneth	Shipping	£12
Short, E.A.	Flowers	£1.50
Sikes, F.H.	General	£1.50
Simkin, R.	Military	£15
Simonetti, A.M.	Glamour	£5
Sinty, Juan	Comic	£1.50
Skip	Comic	£1
Smale, B.H.	Comic	£8

	Military	£8
Small, D.	General	£2
Smith D. Carlton	Children	£5
Smith, Edna	Children	£2
Smith, Jessie Wilcox	Art Nouveau	£35
	Children	£30
Smith, May	Children	£8
Smith, Syd	Comic	£2
Smith, W.	General	£1.50
Smyth	Comic	£1
Sokolov, Yevgeni	General	£10
Solomko, Serge de	Glamour	£20
Somerville, Howard	Glamour	£4
	Comic	£2
Sonrel, Elizabeth	Art Nouveau	£60
Sowerby, Millicent	Children/	
	Chromo-Litho	£20
	Other types	£8
Spatz	Comic	£2
Sperlich, T.	Animals	£6
Spindler, Erwin	General	£6
Spurgin, Fred	Comic	£3
	Glamour	£5
	Military	£5
Spurrier, W.B.	Comic	£2
Spy	Political	£15

Franz Stassen, Wagner series £15

Stanlaw, S. Penrhyn	Glamour	£4
Stanlaws, Penly	Glamour	£6
Stannard, H. Sylvester	General	£2
Stannard, Lilian	General	£2
Stassen, F	Music	£15
Stead, A.	General	£1
Steele, L.	Children	£4
Steinlen, Alexandre	Art Nouveau	£90
Stenberg, Aina	Art Deco	£15
Sternberg, V.W.	Children	£2
Stewart, J.A.	Animals	£5
	Military	£5
Stoddart, R.W.	Comic	£2
Stokes G. Vernon	Animals	£2
Stone, Frederick	Comic	£1.50
Stone, F.	Comic	£2
Stower, Willi	Shipping/	
	Early	£20
	Later	£6
	General	£6
Stretton, Philip	Animals	£5
Strong, G.W.	Comic	£1.50
Studdy, G.E.	Comic/	
	Bonzo	£8
	Others	£6

I'VE JUST REMEMBERED I FORGOT TO WRITE YOU!

George Studdy, Bonzo, £8

Lance Thackeray, Cricket, £10

Sullivan, Pat	Comic	£5
Syd	Comic	£2
Syllikuss	Comic	£2
Symonds, Constance	Children	£8
Szyk, Arthur	Political	£6/£15
T.	Comic	£1
C.T.	Comic	£1.50
J.T.	General	£1.50
L.B.T.	Comic	£1.50
W.E.T.	Comic	£1.50
Tait	Comic	£1
Talboys, A.	Animals	£3
Tam, Jean	Glamour	£12
Tanquerey, L.	Art Deco	£4
Tarrant, Margaret W.	Children/6	
	Pre-1945	£5
	1945 on	£2
Taylor, A.	Children	£1.50
	Comic	£1.50
Taylor, E.S.	Comic	£1.50
Tempest, Douglas	Children	£1.50
	Comic	£1.50
Tempest, Margaret	Children	£3
Terzi, A.	Glamour	£8
Thackeray, Lance	Comic/	
	Write-away	£10
	Oilettes	£5
Theo	Aviation	£20
Thiede, Adolf	General	£1.50
Thiele, Arthur	Animals	£15+
	Comic	£15+
	Political	£25
Thomas, Bert	Comic	£5
Thomas, Paul	Animals	£5

Thomas, Victor	Children	£6			Military	£4
Thomas, Walter	Shipping	£10	Valter, Eugenie M.	Animals	£4
Thompson, E.H.	General	£1.50	Valter, Florence E.	Animals	£4
Thorne, Diana	Animals	£1.50	Vaughan, F H	General	£1.50
Titicus	Comic	£1.50	Veal, O.	Comic	£2
Toussaint, M.	Military	£6	Vera	Children	£2
Travis, Stuart	General	£1.50	Vernon, E.	Glamour	£6
Trick, E.W.	General	£1.50	Vernon, R.W.	General	£1.50
Tringham, H.	General	£1.50	Villon Jacques	Art Nouveau	£300
Trow	Comic	£1	Voellmy, F.	General	£8
True, W.	Theatre	£12	Vouga, E.	Flowers	£1
Truman, Herbert	General	£1	F.W.	Comic	£1.50
Turner, C.E.	Shipping	£8	J.S.W.	Comic	£2

Turrian, E.D.	Art Nouveau	£30	Wain, Louis	Animals/	
Twelvetrees, C.H.	Children	£6		Early	£60+
Uden, E.	General	£1		Later	£40+
Ullman, Max	Shipping	£15		Oilettes	£40+
Underwood,				Advertising	£75+
Clarence F	Glamour	£6	Wal.	Comic	£1.50
Upton, Florence K.	Children	£35	Walbourn, Ernest	General	£1.50
Usabal, Luis	Glamour	£6	Walker, F.S.	General	£1.50
Utrillo, A.	General	£6	Walker, Hilda	Animals	£4
Valles, F.	Comic	£1.50	Wanke, Alice	Art Nouveau	£20
Vallet, L.	Glamour	£10		Children	£10

Ward, Dudley	Comic	£3
Ward, Herbert	Military	£5
Ward, Vernon	General	£1.50
Wardle, Arthur	Animals	£8
Warrington, Ellen	General	£1.50
Watson, C.M. West	Animals	£5
Wealthy, R.J.	Animals	£3
Weaver, E.	Comic	£1.50
Webb, A.D.	General	£1
Weierter, Louis	Advertising	£25
Welzi, A.	Art Nouveau	£30
Wennerberg, Brynolf	Art Nouveau	£20
	Glamour	£15
West, A.L.	Animals	£2
West, Reginald	General	£1.50
Weston, Rita F.	Children	£1
Whatley, H	General	£2
Wheeler, Dorothy	Children	£4
Whishaw, A.Y.	General	£1.50
White, Brian	Children	£2

Herbert Ward, Military £5

	Comic	£2
White, D.	Comic	£2
White, Flora	Children	£5
White, H. Percy	Comic	£2
Whitehead, Fred	General	£1.50
Wichera, R.R.	Children	£6
	Glamour	£8
Wiederseim, G.G.	Children	£6
Wielandt, Manuel	General	£8
Wilcock, A.M.	Children	£4
Wilkin, Bob	Comic	£1
Wilkinson, Gilbert	Comic	£5
Wilkinson, Norman	Shipping	£10
Williams, Madge	Children	£3
Williams, Warren	General	£1.50
Willis, George	Comic	£1.50
Wilson, David	Political	£6
Wimble, Arthur	Glamour	£2
Wimbush, Henry B.	General	£3
Wimbush, Winifred	General	£3
	Glamour	£6

ON THE STARBOARD TACK

Lawson Wood, Comic £6

Wishaw, M.C.	General	£3
Wood, Lawson	Comic	£6
	Gran'pop	£6
	Prehistoric	£6
	Theatre	£18
Wood, Starr	Comic	£5
Woodville, R. Caton	Military	£6
Woollett, Cress	Glamour	£3
Woude Sikko van de	General	£2
Wright, Gilbert	General	£4
Wright, Seppings,	General	£2
Wuyts, A	Children	£6
	Glamour	£6
Wyllie, W.L.	Shipping	£8
H.Y.	Comic	£1.50
Young, A.	General	£1.50
Young Gwen Hayward	General	£3
Young, Hayward	General	£3
Zandrino, Adelina	Glamour	£10
Zirka, C.	Glamour	£6

Henry Wimbush £3

ARTHUR THIELE

Gebruder Dietrich (GDL)

Ser 273.	Ice Sports	£40
Ser 277.	Gentleman & servant	£40
Ser 284.	Whitsun scenes	£40

Friedrich Eyfried (FED)

Ser 474.	Teddy Bears	£50
Ser 486.	Costumes	£50
Ser 525.	Carnival	£30

F&W

| Ser 159. | Fantasy Cats | £40 |

Faulkner C.W.

Ser 1067.	As TSN 1194	£40
Ser 1298.	Musical Cats in Snow	£40
Ser 1373.	As TSN 1423	£20
Ser 1376.	Easter Chicks	£20
Ser 1378.	Springtime in Catland	£40

Klaus & Co.

| Ser 474. | The Nursery | £40 |
| Ser 486. | Ladies' Hats | £40 |

Bruder Kohn (BKW)

| Ser 323. | Sporting Types | £40 |

L&P

Ser 1446.	Kitten Orchestras I	£40
Ser 1447.	Kitten Orchestras II	£40
Ser 1564.	Congratulations	£40
Ser 1566.	Cat Orchestras	£40
Ser 2431.	Du Falsche (1)	£50

Novolito

| Ser 476. | Cat Scenes I | £40 |
| Ser 477. | Cat Scenes II | £40 |

Theo Stroefer (TSN)

Ser 196.	As TSN 1425	£40
Ser 710.	Be-ribboned Cats	£20
Ser 851.	Life at Home	£30
Ser 896.	Cats with Hats	£40
Ser 918.	TheSix Ages of the Cat	£30
Ser 945.	Kittens with Bouquets	£30
Ser 947.	Diabolo	£40
Ser 962.	School Kittens	£20
Ser 975.	Tears and Joy	£25
Ser 995.	Winged Cats	£40
Ser 1010.	Children's Games	£20
Ser 1012.	A Mewsical Party	£20
Ser 1016.	Cats at Play	£40
Ser 1018.	Classic Loves	£40
Ser 1077.	Events at Home	£20
Ser 1113.	Haute Cat-ure	£50
Ser 1194.	Toboggan Rides	£40

Ser 1214.	A Tennis Tournament	£30
Ser 1229.	The Subscription Ball	£30
Ser 1230.	Servants	£40
Ser 1299.	Winter Sports	£50
Ser 1326.	In the Classroom	£20
Ser 1403.	Music in the Snow	£40
Ser 1404.	New Year Greetings	£30
Ser 1405.	New Year Gifts	£40
Ser 1412.	Kittens at Play	£40
Ser 1423.	School Kittens	£20
Ser 1424.	Domestic Service	£30
Ser 1425.	Just like Dad	£40
Ser 1427.	Bowling	£40
Ser 1438.	Spring Scenes	£20
Ser 1468.	Say it with Flowers	£25
Ser 1469.	Fun in Snowland	£30
Ser 1472.	Ice Skating	£30
Ser 1601.	As TSN 1010	£20
Ser 1602.	Street Scenes	£40
Ser 1604.	As TSN 1077	£20
Ser 1646.	As TSN 975	£25
Ser 1667.	As TSN 1010	£20
Ser 1671.	As TSN 1438	£20
Ser 1677.	As TSN 1326	£20
Ser 1703.	As TSN 1424	£30
Ser 1705.	As TSN 1404	£30
Ser 1714.	As TSN 1012	£20
Ser 1726.	As TSN 1423	£20
Ser 1727.	As TSN 1077	£20
Ser 1728.	As TSN 1326	£20
Ser 1730.	As TSN 1424	£30
Ser 1789.	As TSN 1468	£25
Ser 1789.	As TSN 1469	£30
Ser 1800.	As TSN 962	£20
Ser 1826.	As TSN 1423	£20
Ser 1827.	As TSN 1077	£20
Ser 1828.	As TSN 1326	£20
Ser 1829.	As TSN 1438	£20
Ser 1830.	As TSN 975	£25
Ser 1852.	As TSN 1012	£20
Ser 1876.	As TSN 1472	£30
Ser 1879.	As TSN 962	£20
Ser 1880.	As TSN 1423	£20
Ser 1881.	As TSN 1077	£20
Ser 1882.	As TSN 1326	£20
Ser 1889.	As TSN 1438	£20
Ser 1892.	As TSN 1424	£30
Ser 1893.	Puppies	£40
Ser 1988.	Kittens at Play	£40
Ser 1989.	Cats at Play	£40
Ser 2030.	As TSN 962	£20
Ser 2031.	As TSN 1326	£20

Tuck R. & Sons			Other Publishers			
Ser 3435. As TSN 1326		£20	Reproductions are known from the following			
Ser 4091. As TSN 975		£25	publishers:			
Ser 8604. As TSN 1468		£25				
Ser 8604. As TSN 1469		£30				
Ser 9782. As TSN 1229		£30	**C.K.M.**	2641	As TSN 710	£20
Ser 9797. As TSN 1012		£20	**H.B.K.**	609	As F&W 159	£40
Ser 9818. Catland		£40	**J.S**	2641	As TSN 710	£20
Ser 9819. Playtime		£40	**K&BC**	3105	As FED 525	£30
Ser 9983. As TSN 1214		£30	**KF**	3076	As TSN 851	£30

Arthur Thiele produced a style of art which proved very popular and many of these series were reproduced both by the original publisher and by others who bought the rights. The same series may therefore be found several times under different imprints. Building on the work of Mr. Gerd Schwartz and Dr. Ronald Hendrickson, I have started listing all known series for future catalogue entry.

All prices above are for single cards. A complete set may attract a premium over this figure. It must be noted that prices apply to cards in flawless condition, with no marks or damage of any kind.

Above: Series 1155 Billiards. £20
Right:Series 1988 £40
Below Left: No.70 £20
Below Right: Aviation £40

Published by Tuck No 9396 £45

Cat's Acadamy, W E Mack £30

*Contented, Tuck'
series 9501 £40*

Tuck's 'Calendar' No.5802 £35

Inter Art, 'Kitty' Series £45

Valentines, Series £40

LOUIS WAIN

Beagles
Coloured & Photographic £35

Boots
Famous Picture Series of 12 £35

Davidson Bros.
Various Cards £40

Dutton/N.Y.
Various Cards £35

Ettlinger & Co.
Series 5226. Father Christmas Cats £80
Series 5376. Father Christmas Cats £80

Faulkner C.W.
Series 182 • 183 • 189 • 190 • 374
453 • 454 • 484 • 485 • 503 • 515
541 • 1596 • plus many others. £35/£50

Gale & Polden
At least 1 design £45

Hartmann
Series 3068. Fluffikins Family £45
Series 3069. Manx Cats £60

Mack W.E.
The Cat's Academy (Not all by Wain) £30

Nister E.
Series 353 • 355 etc. £35
Valentine series £6

Philco series 2093 £35

Salmon series various cards £35

Theo Stroefer
Usually unsigned designs £25

Tuck R. & Sons
Series 130. Black/White und. back £20

Theatre Series 3885 • 3895 B/W £45

Write-Away Series
539 • 956 • 957 • 1003 • 1004 £35

Chromo-Litho Series
1260 • 1261 • 1262 • 1735 • 1748
1749 • 1782 • 5802 • 5892 £30

Chromo-Litho Nursery Rhymes/
Christmas/Pantomime
Series 297 • 298 • 8126 • 8127 £100

Diabolo Series 9563 £45

Dressing Dolls Fairy Tales
Oilette 3385 £100+

Oilette and similar Series
1412 • 3266 • 6075 • 6084 • 6401
6444 • 8515 • 8612 • 8613 • 8614
8615 • 8816 • 8817 • 8826 • 8850
8864 • 9396 • 9540 • 9541 £35

Others/Odd cards/
Part Sets inc. C132/133 £30

Valentine
Coloured Series/Un-numbered £40
Charlie Chaplin cards £100

Wrench
Pantomime/Black Cat Series £50

Anon
Jackson's Hats & Boots/Poster Type £75
WW1 Set including a cat `Kaiser' £75

Many other cards exist, sometimes pirate copies, often with Wain's signature removed. There are also a number of unsigned cards by other artists done in the Wain style.
All prices above are for single cards.
A complete set may attract a premium over this figure.
It must be noted that prices apply to cards in flawless condition, with no marks or damage of any kind.

Philco, Series 2083 £60

AVIATION

The early days of flying presented a challenge which postcard publishers were not slow to take up, with the resulting legacy of a great many fine studies both photographic and artistic on this theme. Postcards cover the whole spectrum of civil and military aviation from the early beginnings, through World War I to the nineteen thirties and up to the present day. Generally speaking photographic cards are worth more than artistic studies, the former often having some related local history interest. It must be further emphasised that in all cases prices given are for unused cards. If postally used a much higher figure may be expected, depending upon type of postmark, date of flight, clarity of strike etc.

Market Report:
Every year it's tempting to ask 'When will this category take off?' Early photographic cards with local topographical interest can command high prices. Post war airport scenes and semi modern civil aviation are popular.

AIRCRAFT

AIRCRAFT Pre-1918

Flying at Hendon Series	£12
Brooklands Aviation	£20
Daily Mail Tour 1912	£10
At named locations	£30
French Aviation	£8
Civil aircraft	£10
Military aircraft	£8

Accidents
Identified	£25
Unidentified	£5

Series
Lefebvre Utile	£35
Lombart	£25

Educational Series
Tuck R. & Sons	£20

The Lightning Series
E. Cook	£15

Famous Aeroplane Series
Tuck R. & Sons	£5

In the Air Series
Tuck R. & Sons	£6

Artist/Derek Bannister
Salmon J. Ltd	£5

AIRCRAFT 1918-1939

Schneider Trophy	£20+
Civil Aircraft	£10-15
Military Aircraft	£5-10
Joy Flights	£6-8

Accidents
Identified	£25
Unidentified	£5

Amy Johnson
England-Australia Flight/Set 6/ Tuck R. & Sons/3867B	£15
Portraits	£15

Imperial Airways
Croydon Airport	£18
Official	£18
Pilots	£20

AIRCRAFT 1939 - 1960
Civil Aircraft	£8-15

Real Photograph Series
Valentine	£3

PILOTS
Pre-1914
With aircraft	£15
Portraits	£12

1918-1939
With aircraft	£15
Portraits	£12

Imperial Airways Liner, Hannibal. Pr. £5

Joyriding at Blackpool   Pr. £12

Aviation meeting at Champagne 1909 Pr £15

Bournemouth Aviation Meting R/P £25

M. Lefebre, National Series Pr. £10

The first newspaper aeroplane delivery service £35

Booking Hall Croydon Aerodrome R/P £18

G.V.Hamel, Pilot of the first aerial post Pr £20

Croydon Aerodrome R/P £20

Imperial Airways 'City of Manchester' 19 Passengers and a range of 400 miles R/P £18

Cornwall Aviation Avro 504K , used for pilot training c.1936 R/P £18

Westland 'Limousine', able to carry three passengers or 540lbs of mail £18

*Top; BEA advertising card, R/P £5.
BOAC 'Britannia' £6, Salmon Series- Avro 652 £5,
'Golden Ray' at Croydon R/P £20,
Short Brothers 'Empire' seaplane R/P £6*

AVIATION MEETINGS

Blackpool 1909/10	£20
Doncaster 1909	£30
Bournemouth 1910	£25
Burton on Trent 1910	£40
Lanark 1910	£40
Wolverhampton 1910	£40

Doncaster Pilots 1909, £30

Poster Adverts

Coloured	£60
Black & White	£30
Early Airline Poster Adverts	**£85**

FLOWN CARDS

Beckenham Coronation Balloon/9.8.02
Flown	
Unflown	

Lifeboat Saturday/20.9.02
Flown	£1,000
Unflown	£100

Lifeboat Saturday/29.8.03
Flown	£1,000
Unflown	£100

Daily Graphic Expedition 1907
Flown	£150
Unflown	£50

First U.K. Aerial Post 1911
London-Windsor - Flown	£20/£40
Windsor-London - Flown	£30/£75
Unflown cards	£18

N.B. The value of flown U.K. Aerial Post Cards depends upon which colour type has been used, date of flight, clarity of strike etc. These factors are also relevant to any flown cards.

AIRSHIPS

At named locations	£30
World Flights	£25

GB/Pre-1918
Barton Airship/Alexandra Palace 1905	£35
Beta/Gamma/Parseval etc.	£18

GB/1918-1939
R-100/R-101 etc.	£18

French/German
Pre-1918	£15
1918-1939	£15

Zeppelins
Early Chromo embossed etc.	£25+
World War 1/ Close-up	£18
/Combat sketches	£5
Wreckage/GB Locations	£10

Tuck's Aviation, Zeppelin £25

BALLOONS

At named locations	£65
Photographic	£35+
Printed	£20
Military/Printed	£8
Swiss/Meetings Posters	£75+

MISCELLANEOUS

Airfields	£8-12
R.F.C. Interest	£5-8

Commemorative Cards
First/Historic Flights	£25+

Croydon Airport
C.H. Price Series	£20

Royal Air Force
Halton Camp	£8
Airmen/Photographs Identified	£5
/Unidentified	£1.50
Miscellaneous interest	£1.50

MILITARY AIRCRAFT

Lieut. Brandon, M.C., D.S.O., Pr £15

General Sir David Henderson in comand of the RFC £15

Nulli Secondis, Printed £6
Flew from Aldershot to London in 1907
Britain's first military airship.

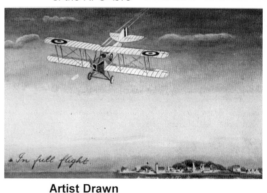

Artist Drawn

Tuck R. & Sons In The Air	£4/6
Celesque Series	£4/6
Mack W.E.	£4
Salmon J.	£4

Real Photographic

Flight	£3
Aircraft Manufacturing Co. Series R/P	£8
Valentines	£5

Royal Flying Corps, James Henderson & Sons £9.50

HM Airship 'Silver Queen', RP £12

SalmonSeries, Hawker Hurricane £3

Airships

Nulli Secundus Pr.Photo c.1907	£6
Beta/Gamma	£12/£15
Zeppelins Close-up	£18
Combat sketches	£3/5
Wreckage/GB Locations	£8

Aircraft

Royal Flying Corp 1912-18
Royal Naval Air Service 1914-18

Pilots/Machines	£10/12
Groups/Machines named Sqdn.	£15/20
Aces/Machines	£20
Portraits	£12/15

R.F.C. & R.N.A.S. amalgamated in 1918 to become the Royal Air Force.

1918-1939	£5
1939-1960	£3

Miscellaneous

Airfields/Hangers	£8
Bombers/Fighters	£3
Flying Boats	£5
Gliders	£3

Aircraft Manufacturing Co. Series R/P £8

Royal Flying Corps, Daily Mail R/P £6

CHILDREN

One of the most popular themes for the early publishers of picture postcards, reflecting the tastes of our Edwardian forbears. Cards of Children and related subjects were published by the thousand. Perhaps the best known series is the 'Queen's Dolls House', published by Tuck, while many of the early chromo-litho art studies, in their design and execution represent some of the most beautiful cards ever printed.

Market Report
Endearing photographic studies of little girls are about all the market can tolerate at present. Better fairy cards will always sell but at more modest price levels than in the past.

CHILDREN

Angels
Art studies	£3
Photographic	£1.50

Babies £1
Perambulators	£5

Fairies
Art Studies	£6

Named artists can command a considerable premium
Photographic	£2

Nursery Rhymes
Art Studies	£4
R. Caldecott	£1.50

Named artists can command a considerable premium

Chromo-Litho studies
These range from quite ordinary types to spectacular cards, again with named artists at a premium.
Price range from £3 - £18

Photographic Studies £1-£3

Tuck R. & Sons
Fairy Tales/Art Series 3472	£25
Ping Pong in Fairyland/	
Art Series 1156	£35

Frederick Warne & Co.
Caldecott R./8 sets of 6/	
Nursery Rhymes	£1.50

DOLLS

Close-up photos	£6
Greetings type	£2

Mirror Grange
Tuck R. & Sons	£3

Queen's Dolls House
Tuck R. & Sons/Set 48
Price per card	£1
Complete Set	£60
Wembley Exhibition	£3

Titania's Palace
Tuck R. & Sons/
Two sets of 8 cards	£3
Gale & Polden	£2

Nursery Rhyme by H. Willebeek Le Mair £8

TOYS

Bramber Museum	£1.50
Diabolo sketches	£5
Golliwogs	£15+
Close-up photos	£6
Greetings type	£2

Teddy Bears
Art Studies	£12
Photographic	£8
Pullouts	£15
Roosevelt Cartoons	£30

Chromo Litho £8

THE LOG GATHERERS.

Rene Cloke £8

OFF TO THE FAIR

Margaret Tarrant £5

Hand Tinted Real Photographic £3

CINEMA

Not a subject much in evidence during the hey-day of the picture postcard, the majority of Film Stars we find today date from the 1920-1939 period. The 'Picturegoer' series is very popular, while other collectors look for individual Stars.

Market Report
There are large quantities of unwanted 1930's and 1940's stars that are having a dampening effect on the whole market. Selectively, good prices can still be obtained but the market seems past its heyday.

FILM STARS

This is a select list of names, whom because of scarcity or demand, are currently fetching prices in excess of Catalogue valuation.

Abbott and Costello	£15
Astaire, Fred	£4
Ball, Lucille	£6
Bergman, Ingrid	£9
Bogart, Humphrey	£6
Brando, Marlon	£10
Brooks, Louise	£35
Cagney, James	£5
Chaplin, Charlie	£7
Comic sketches	£6
Red Letter Stills	£3
Cole, Nat King	£12
Davis, Bette	£9
Dean, James	£12
Dietrich, Marlene	£8
Dors, Diana	£10
Durante, Jimmy	£8
Fields, W.C.	£8
Flynn, Errol	£6
Formby, George	£8
Gable, Clark	£4
Garbo, Greta	£4
Garland, Judy	£9
Betty Grable	£7.50
Harlow, Jean	£7.50
Hepburn, Audrey	£15
Holliday, Judy	£8
Howerd, Frankie	£8
Jolson, Al	£8
Keaton, Buster	£6
Kelly, Grace	£6
Lamour, Dorothy	£8
Lanza, Mario	£8
Laurel & Hardy	£25
Leigh, Vivien	£10
Lloyd, Harold	£5
Lombard, Carole	£6
Loren, Sophia	£8
Mansfield, Jayne	£6
Marx Bros.	£15
Monroe, Marilyn	£25
Presley, Elvis	£12

Paul Robeson	£15
Robinson, Edward G.	£7.50
Rogers Ginger	£6
Temple, Shirley	£4
Valentino, Rudolph	£4
Wayne, John	£7
Welles, Orson	£8
West, Mae	£9.50
Wisdom, Norman	£6

Laurel & Hardy R/P   £25

Series

Dave and Dusty	£3
Pictures Portrait Gallery	£2
Cinema Chat	£2
Picturegoer/1921-1939	£3
/1940-1962	£5

The Picturegoer Series ran to 6600 cards, published from 1921 to c.1962.

Film Sets/Stills

Pre-1939	£4
1940 onwards	£6

Picturegoer and other firms also produced six-card sets of scenes from individual films. Prices for the most part follow those of the respective Stars.

Miscellaneous Publishers

Pre-1939	£2
1940 onwards	£4
Continental Stars	£2
Coral-Lee 1980	£1

With all Film Star postcards, the value is determined by the name of the artist. Cards of the 1940's and 1950's are in most demand, and a price of £4 would be realistic for the majority of artists from this period. For cards of the 1920's and 1930's, a corresponding figure would be £2. But there are exceptions as given in our select list, and including certain other names of significance, or with a cult following. As a rule of thumb, the well-known Star is worth more than the unknown.

Please note that plain back cards carry the same value as postcard backs.

Above: Humphrey Bogart R/P £6

Danny Kaye R/P £7.50

Norma Shearer, R/P £6

Autographs / Ink Signed

Value is determined by the individual Star. Certain names are worth more than others. Advice from a specialist is recommended.

CINEMA

MISCELLANEOUS

Bioscopes	£50
Cinemas	£35
Felix the Cat	£12

Cinema Organists

Dixon, Reginald	£5
Others	£4

Disney

Mickey Mouse/Picturegoer Series Nos.	
452, 452a, 452b	£50
Foreign published/France/Holland	£8+
Other Disney issues	£8+

Bambi, Published by Valentines, £12

"I won't be home 'till morning!"

Felix the
Cat £12

Judy Garland, Show Parade R/P £9

Louise Brooks, R/P £35

COMIC

The Comic postcard is a British institution. It is the yardstick by which most non-collectors judge our hobby! Everyone recognises the Comic card, with its bygone images of hen-pecked husbands, red-nosed drunks, saucy jokes, and embarrassed Vicars! It has been the subject of learned dissertations by authors as varied as George Orwell to Ronnie Barker. And yet, with the exception of a few named Artists or themes allied to other subjects, Comic cards are not as popular today as in former times.

Market Report

This is a secondary collecting theme for many collectors who obviously consider some of these prices a bit of a joke. Jewish, Masonic, Golf and Cameras are popular but most types need to be a bit more sensibly priced to sell..

SERIES

Bamforth & Co.

Pre 1918	£2
1918-1939	£2
1940 onwards	£1

Tuck R & Sons

Write Away/Early Vignettes	£10
Write Away/Later Issues	£4

Fragments from France/
B. Bairnsfather

Numbers 1 - 48	£3
Numbers 49-54	£10

Sketches of Tommy's Life/
F. Mackain

Set 10/In Training	£3
Set 10/Up the Line	£3
Set 10/Out on Rest	£3
Set 10/At the Base	£3

Black Humour
Happy Little Coons/Tuck R. & Sons/

Oilettes/H.D. Sandford	£12
Other Black Humour	£8

Other Series

Write Off Series/Valentine	£5
Other 'Write-Away' Series	£5

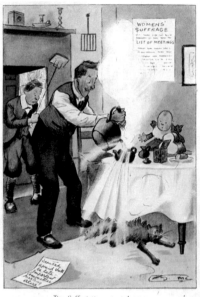

The Suffragette not at home

Suffragette £25

Jewish humour £25

GENERAL

All unsigned cards of general interest may be grouped together into the periods listed below, with this suggested price structure.

Pre-1918	£1.50
1918-1939	£1
1940-1960	.50

Early/Chromo-Litho

Undivided back	£8
Divided Back	£3

COMIC

Lawson Wood £6

George Studdy, 'Bonzo' £8

Suffragette,   £25

Reg Maurice 'Black Humour' £8

TYPES

Listed below are suggested minimum prices, bearing in mind that certain Artist signed may be worth considerably more.

MUFFIN PLAYING CRICKET

KHAKI ALL OVER THE PLACE.

Top; Muffin the Mule, TV £4
Above; Fred Spurgin £5

Angling	£3
Aviation	£3
Billiards/Snooker	£9
Blacks	£8
Cameras	£8
Card Games	£5
Cats	£2
Chess	£15
Cigarette Packets	£8
Corkscrews	£8
Cricket	£9
Crossword Puzzles	£5
Cycling	£3/£6
Dentistry	£10
Diabolo	£3
Dialect	£1
Drinking/Drinks etc.	£2
Erotic	£5
Fleas	£1.50
Football	£6
Golfing	£12
Got Any Cigarette Cards	£12
Gramophones	£5
Hatpins	£1.50
Hunting	£2
Jewish	£25
Lavatorial	£2
Limericks	£4
Maps	£3
Masonic	£20
Match Boxes	£6
Strikers	£15
Military	
Pre-1914	£2
World War 1	£3
World War 2	£5
Miscellaneous	£1.50
Motorcycling	£6
Motoring	£5
Obscene/Sexual	£3
Pawnbrokers	£5
Ping Pong	£20
Playing Cards	£5
Police	£4
Postal	£4
Postcards	£5
Postmen	£5
Prehistoric	£2
Pussyfoot	£3
Racing	£5
Railways	£2
Rinking	£3
Rugby football	£6
Scouts	£10
Smoking	£3
Suffragettes	£25
Telegrams	£3
Telephone	£3
Television	£4
Tennis	£8
Trams	£3
Wireless/Radio	£6
Irish	£3
Scottish	£3
Welsh	£3

Game Of Nap by Tom Browne £5

EARLY CARDS

Postcards were first introduced by Austria in 1869, the first British postcard appearing on 1st October 1870. These were officially issued plain cards with a printed stamp and without a picture, and came to be known as postal stationery. The idea spread rapidly, and within a few years many countries were issuing these novel plain cards. On the Continent, shortly after their introduction, privately issued picture cards came into being, published in varying sizes, but it was not until 1st September 1894 that similar picture cards were permitted in Great Britain, being accepted by the Post Office one month later. These early British cards were known as Court Size. They were smaller and squarer in shape, being issued from 1894-1902, and led to an Intermediate Size from 1898-1902. Until 1902 all cards had to carry the message on the front and the address on the back, thus restricting the design on the card to that of a small picture, or 'vignette', with the rest of the surface left free for writing. But on 1st January, 1902, after mounting pressure from commercial interests, Britain became the first country to divide the back, thus permitting both message and address on this side, leaving the front of the card free for a picture. This move saw the adoption of a universal Standard Size of 5.5 x 3.5in, and heralded the real beginning of picture postcards as a major collecting pastime. Other countries quickly followed, and the resultant explosion in picture postcard production world wide lasted until 1914, when the First World War brought an end to this 'Golden Age'. This is the most complex heading in Postcards, impossible to catalogue in any depth, covering as it does many millions of undivided back cards published throughout the world from 1869-1907, by which latter date all countries had divided the back and adopted the Standard Size. The entries below will form a general guide to type and price for all Early Cards.

Market Report
The serious collectors of these cards are in hibernation as there is little quality material on the market. Anything outstanding should test these prices. Condition is vital.

GREAT BRITAIN
POSTAL STATIONERY/PRE-1894
First Day of Issue Postcard

p.u. 1st October 1870	£400
Unused	£5

Penny Postage Jubilee/Red Card

p.u. May 1890/Guildhall	£50
Unused	£25

Penny Postage Jubilee/& Cover

p.u. July 1890/S. Kensington	£25+
Unused	£8

COURT SIZE/1894-1902
Gruss Aus type   £25

Early Vignettes

Coloured	£25
Sepia/bw	£12

Postally Used
When the above cards are found postally used before 1897, this consideration of early usage would usually over-ride other factors. The prices given below may be taken as a general guide:

1896	£40
1895	£60
1894	£250
September 1894	£400

With all cards from 1895 onwards, certain rare types may fetch prices in excess of those given above.

INTERMEDIATE SIZE/1898-1902
Early Vignettes

Coloured	£15
Sepia/bw	£6

GB Views

Sepia/bw	£2

STANDARD SIZE/1899-1902
Gruss Aus type   £20

Early Vignettes

Coloured	£12
Sepia/bw	£4

GB Views

Sepia/bw	£2

If postally used, a small premium may be added to the above prices. It will be seen that some over-lapping occurs in the periods of usage for these cards. This is because there are examples of different sizes known. With regard to the entry for GB Views, it may be added that the majority of these published before 1902, were mass produced common scenes of large cities, towns and holiday areas, and consequently of little interest to Topographical collectors.

FOREIGN
POSTAL STATIONERY/PRE-1894
First Day of Issue Postcard

p.u. 1st Oct. 1869	£400
Unused	£12

GRUSS AUS/EARLY VIGNETTES

Anniversaries	£25
Festivals	£20
Heraldic	£12
Parades	£18
Souvenirs	£15

Bierhaus at Ente, £15

Early Vignettes

Coloured	£10
Sepia/bw	£2

For postally used cards a modest premium may be added, in keeping with the scale printed under `Gruss Aus/Topographical'.

Early Chromo, Helgoland, postally used 1893 £20

GRUSS AUS/TOPOGRAPHICAL

A difficult area to catalogue, for prices are governed by country of issue, design, condition, and if used date of postmark. The prices given below may be taken as a general indication of value for cards issued in Germany, Austria, Italy and Switzerland, although cards from the smaller towns here are usually worth more than those from large cities.

Fewer Gruss Aus cards were issued by other countries, and as a general rule, the more obscure the country, the higher the value of its cards, with those from places such as the German Colonies, Greece, Palestine, Singapore, and small islands forming the top price bracket of perhaps three times above our base rate.

Prices given apply to postally used cards, although this factor has little significance with later issues from 1896 onwards. Before this date, however, considerations of early usage leading to the field of postcard history may be felt to be of primary importance.

1869-1879	£60
1880-1884	£45
1885-1889	£40
1890-1895	£20
1896-1900+	£12

Nurnberg £25

Sepia/Black & White

From 1896 onwards the production of Gruss Aus (Greetings From) cards increased dramatically.

Those listed above are usually printed chromo-litho in solid colours from 1896 onwards, and in colour and shades of sepia before this date.

From 1896 we find a great many sepia and black & white cards bearing the legend `Gruss Aus', but these are not worth anything like the superb coloured examples. Their average price would be £2.

ETHNIC

Dealing with the races and peoples of the world, this subject was not much in evidence during the early days of collecting, this subject heading covers a fairly broad spectrum of topics mainly showing people in action throughout the world, similar to Social History in Britain. Although before photographic representation of the European Nude became permissible in France during the latter years of World War 1, the many similar studies of native girls offered a culturally acceptable, if hypocritical alternative.

Market Report
Photographic Aborigines and native Americans, French colonial glamour and Russian types are all in short supply. South African studies are not wanted but there are stirrings on the Indian subcontinent at last.

ETHNIC GLAMOUR
Cards in this section show girls either topless or semi-clothed.

Ceylon	£10
Ethiopia	£6
South Africa	£3
Sudan	£6
West Africa	£6
India	£10
Japan	£10

Egypt
Tuck R. & Sons/Oilette 7200/

Egypt - The Sphinx	£3
Miscellaneous types	£5

Senegal

Fortier/Dakar	£8

North Africa
The source of the great majority of Ethnic Glamour cards, depicting mainly Arab or Bedouin girls. The leading publisher was Lehnert & Landrock of Cairo and Tunis.

Lehnert & Landrock

Coloured/Numbered on front	£6
/Other series	£6
Sepia/Numbered on front	£3
Real Photographic	£6
Black & White	£3

Other Publishers

ELD/LL/ND/Geiser	£8
Real Photographic	£6
Miscellaneous types	£3

The following cards show girls fully clothed, but are different to the usual National Dress or Trades and Workers types in that they are specifically intended as glamour studies of beautiful girls in the context of their Ethnic background.

Europe	£1.50
Far East	£1.50
North Africa	£1.50

Cards may be found in both categories from certain other countries - Java, Indo China, Japan etc. Depending upon the image, such cards may be rated slightly higher than the above figures.

Aborigine R/P £6

American Indian, Tuck's £8

Morocco £6

MISCELLANEOUS

American Indians	£8
Cannibals	£10
Cowboys	£5
Fakirs/Snake Charmers	£4
Hats	£2
Opium Smokers	£5
Oxford University Robes	£1.50

Contemporary Fashion
c.1910 Family Portraits	£3

Curiosities
Houses/Models etc.	£2
Natural/Trees etc.	£2

Great Britain
Portraits of People/Groups	£2

Ireland
Irish Humour	£3
People/Costume/Life etc.	£3

Japan
Chromo-Litho vignettes	£12
Hand Painted/Black & Gold	£6
/Other types	£4
Art cards	£3
Art Reproductions/Hiroshige etc.	£1.50
Museum cards	£1
Geisha	£4
People/Costume/Life etc.	£1.50
Temples/Cherry Blossom etc.	£1

Masonic
Are You a Mason?/24 cards
Millar & Lang	£20
Regalia/Miscellaneous	£8

National Dress
Misch & Stock/Stengel etc.	£1.50
Miscellaneous types	£1

Native Races
South American Indians	£5
Other Native Tribes	£5
Local Industries	£2
People/Costume/Life etc.	£1.50

Russia
Types of Russian Life	£10
People/Costume/Art	£3

Scotland
Types of Scottish Dress/Castle Series	£5
Scottish Humour	£2
Highland Washing scenes	£2
People/Costume/Life etc.	£1.50

Wales
Welsh Humour	£2
People/Costume/Life etc.	£2

See also 'Ethnic' listing under individual countries.

JEWISH POSTCARDS

The subjects of Jewish postcards range from New Year's greeting cards, Synagogues & Palestine, to those featuring specific Jewish themes like Jewish Holidays, famous Jewish people and Rabbis.

Famous Jewish Writers, scarce £18

SYNAGOGUES

This is a very collectable subject.

The synagogues of Germany, Austria and East Europe are very much in demand especially the ones that were destroyed during the Pogroms & Second World War.
(£30 - £40)

Northern American & French Synagogues are more common and therefore less desirable.
(£8 - £10)

Synagogue, Antwerp £15

Many of the images were staged, often featuring models that made multiple appearances in different settings but they faithfully represented realistic elements of daily life.

"Happy New Year" in Hebrew, English and Yiddish, and a short poem was often added.
(£5 - £10)

Synagogue in Cleveland Ohio
Cleveland News Company 1907 £10

PALESTINE

Most of the postcards of Palestine are topographical or historical. They are mainly cards of towns and street scenes. Some postcards mark special occasions like a visit of an important person etc.
(£5 - £10)

The New Years greeting cards that were published in Poland & Russia are rare and therefore more valuable.
(£30 - £60)

New Years Card in Hebrew , English & Yiddish Poem. Williamsburg Art & co 1910. Early Zionist £12

Awaiting Balfour, in Tel Aviv near the Triumph Gate. Moshe Ordmann 1925 £10

NEW YEARS GREETING CARDS

Sending Jewish New Years cards has always been very popular. Most of the cards had no specific Jewish motive but the pictures were taken from different sources.

New Years Card in Hebrew , English & Yiddish Poem £9

EXHIBITIONS

A vast and complex field with many Exhibitions well able to support their own specialised Catalogue. All the events listed below had picture postcards issued, some of which were sold at retail outlets throughout the country, quite removed from the Exhibition itself. All one can do here is to list the main events, and give a suggested minimum price per card, bearing in mind that certain cards may be worth more if depicting Trade Stands, carrying Advertisements, or bearing an Artist's signature. This whole section needs to be re-done by an expert in the field

Market Report
This section is experiencing something of a revival. If you can plough your way through the common material, there is now strong demand for anything unusual, particularly from the 1908 Franco-British and 1924 Wembley exhibitions. The same can not be said for anything foreign unfortunately.

GREAT BRITAIN

Royal Naval Exhibition/S.W.
Eddystone Lighthouse
p.u.1891/Violet postmark — £75
p.u. 1891/Blue postmark — £75

Gardening & Forestry Exhibition
Eddystone Lighthouse
p.u. 1893/Earls Court — £150
Unused — £75

Victorian Era 1897
Earls Court — £50

Women's Exhibition 1900
Earls Court/Dinka Village — £5

Glasgow 1901
Cassiers H. — £8
bw views — £4

Military 1901
Earls Court — £6

Cork 1902 — £5

Wolverhampton 1902 — £6

Highland & Jacobite 1903
Inverness — £5

International Fire 1903
Earls Court — £5

Scottish Home Industries 1903
Manchester — £5

Bradford 1904 — £3

International Gas 1904
Earls Court — £5

Italian 1904
Earls Court — £3

Nottingham 1904
Fire scenes/General views — £3

Colonial 1905
Crystal Palace — £5

Imperial Austrian 1906
Earls Court — £1.50

Balkan States 1907
Earls Court — £3

Irish International 1907
Dublin — £3

South African Products 1907
Poster Advert Card — £12

Crystal Palace 1908 — £4

Hungarian 1908 — £2

Scottish National 1908
Edinburgh — £2

Worlds Mining 1908
Olympia — £3

Franco-British 1908
Mucha — £150
Woven Silk — £50
Trade Stands — £8
Hagenbeck Circus/Stadium — £5
Comic/Patriotic — £4
Views — £1.50

Imperial International 1909
Trade Stands — £8
Patriotic/Tartar Camp — £5
Views — £1.50

C.M.S. Africa & The East 1909
Islington — £3

Golden West 1909
Earls Court — £3

Japan-British 1910
Trade Stands — £8
Comic/Patriotic — £3
Views — £2

Coronation 1911
Trade Stands — £8
White City Views — £2

Festival of Empire 1911
Oxo/Patriotic — £8
Crystal Palace/Views — £3

Scottish National 1911
Glasgow — £2

Jubilee International Stamp 1912
Victoria S.W./Ideal Stamp — £10

Latin-British 1912
White City — £1.50

Shakespeare's England 1912
Earls Court   £1.50

Building Trades 1913
Olympia   £3

Imperial Services 1913
Earls Court   £3

Liverpool 1913   £3

Russian Village 1913
Olympia   £3

Anglo-American 1914
Band/Patriotic/Wild West   £5
White City/Views   £2

Anglo-Spanish 1914
Earls Court   £3

Bristol International 1914   £3

Newcastle upon Tyne 1929   £3

Empire 1938
Glasgow   £1.50

Festival of Britain 1951
Signed Watercolours   £8
Far Tottering & Oyster Creek Railway £5
Views   £3
Miscellaneous Exhibitions
Daily Mail/Flower Shows etc.   £1.50
Cards printed on Stands   £8

BRITISH EMPIRE 1924/25
Advertising Cards
Cope Bros/Poster Adverts   £50
Tuck R. & Sons by C.E. Flower/
APOC/North British Rubber/
Bryant & May/Sharp's etc.   £12
Anchor Line/HMV etc.   £12

Court & Pavilion cards
Australia/Bengal/Bombay etc.   £3
Falklands Court   £50

Ghent 1913 £12

British Empire 1925 £12

British Empire 1924 £3

Scottish National 1911 £3

Exhibition views		PAGEANTS/OVERSEAS	
Tuck R. & Sons/Coloured	£3	**Quebec 1908**	£2
Fleetway/Sepia	£1.50	**Hudson-Fulton 1909**	£5
Other Publishers/RP & Coloured	£1.50	**Capetown 1910**	£2
/Sepia	£1.50	**National Fetes**	£3

Colonial views

Tuck R & Sons/RP	£3
/Coloured	£3
/Sepia	£2
Other Publishers/Sepia	£1.50

Queens Doll's House

Tuck R. & Sons	£3

Milano 1906   £5

Franco British Exhibition 1908 £1.50

PAGEANTS U/K   £2

For full listings of UK and overseas Pageants see Picture postcard values 2003

Worlds Fair 1934, Firestone Advert £15

OVERSEAS EXHIBITIONS

With hundreds of overseas Exhibitions held world-wide during the past century, it is neither realistic nor practical to attempt to list every single one, let alone give prices for all their cards. Many of these Exhibitions could support their own Catalogue! As for pricing, any attempt at this is dependent upon knowing exactly what was published, and this information is not yet in the public domain. As a general guide the following price structure may be of some help:

1881-1895	**£20/£40**
1896-1900	**£10/£20**
1901-1905	**£2/£8**
1906-1918	**£1/£5**
1919 onwards	**£1/£3**

Any pre-1907 card of Gruss Aus design would be worth at least £10, but other early bw or sepia cards such as those from Paris 1900 would be valued at around £1.50. It must be further pointed out that the unusual or spectacular card, such as a Poster Advert, from any Exhibition may be worth considerably more than its range given above while at the same time some Exhibitions may be more popular than others.

EXPLORATION

The explorations and expeditions of the Edwardian Age were well covered by the picture post-cards of the time, albeit in smaller production runs than the more popular themes. For this reason the cards which remain are difficult to find and consequently highly priced.

Market Report

Prices have been frozen due to a lack of material on the market.

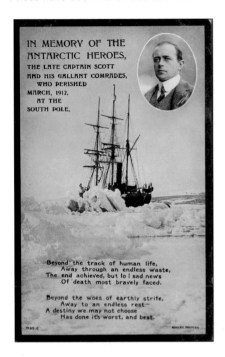

*Above left;
Scott
memorium card
R/P £30
Above Top: LL
series 'Le
Francais' £25
Above;
Meissner &
Buch series
1016 'Fram'
£25. Left; 1897
Andree expedi-
tion Pr. £60*

POLAR

All prices are for unused cards; beware modern reproductions.

Cards sent from expeditions carry a large premium.

ANTARCTIC

1897-99 de Gerlache (Belgium)

Set 12 pub. Nels each	£25
Return of expedition 1899	£40
Various cards	£30

1901 Drygalski (Germany)

Set 5 Artist drawn cards each	£125

1901-04 Nordenskjold (Sweden)

Set 10 'S.Y.Antarctic' exp. each	£60
Argentine rescue cards various	£50

1901-04 Scott

Set 4 Wrench Links of Empire

p.u. from ports of call each	£150
Set 24 Canterbury Times each	£45
Set 12 Weekly Press each	£80
Ship 'Discovery' various	£25

1903-05 Charcot (France)

Set 6 for subscribers (Tuck) p.u. each	£100
Launch of 'Francais'1903	£40
Set 20 Expedition cards each	£50
Various cards of ship 'Francais'	£30

1904 Scottish National Expedition

Set 12 pub W.Ritchie each	£50
Various pub. in Argentina	£40
Ship 'Scotia' various	£35

1907-09 Shackleton

Set 12 expedition views each	£20
With printed adverts	£30
Ship 'Nimrod' various photos	£25+
Shackleton various photos	£20

1908-10 Charcot (France)

Launch of 'Pourquoi-Pas?'	£40
Various ship cards pub ELD, ND	£30
Expedition cards	£50

1910-12 Amundsen (Norway)

Set 5 chromo-litho pub Mittet each	£20
Amundsen photo	£25

1910-13 Scott

Set 12 Ponting photos each	£25
Memoriam cards Rotary / Batchelder	£15/30
Various NZ pub ship 'Terra Nova'	£50
Advertising cards Fry, Shell, etc	£60
Memorials to Scott, statues, cairns etc	£8
Expedition memorial cards, various	£25

Ponting Series 1913,   £25

1914-17 Shackleton

Set 8 sepia expedition photos each	£20
With Spratts dog food advert each	£30
Ship 'Endurance' in port	£40
Various Return of Expedition cards	£50

1921-22 Shackleton –Rowett Expedition

'Quest' at Portsmouth	£70
Various departure, crew members etc	£50
Shackleton's grave 1929	£15

1928-30, 1933-35 Byrd (USA).)

Set 17sepia photos 1929,each p.u.1934	£20
Set dog teams pub Neill NZ 1928 each	£60
1933 Fair 'City of New York' ship	£5
Expedition dogs, various	£10

1954 Australia research expedition

Map card	£10
Set 5 photos pub Seven Seas each	£10

1955-58   Trans-Antarctic   Expedition

Set 7 b/w photos each	£10+

The standard catalogue on Antarctic postcards is 'Postcards of Antarctic Expeditions' by Margery Wharton. For further details email- margery.wharton@tesco.net

ARCTIC

1893 Nansen (Norway)
Composite Set 4/Price per Set	£400
On board the `Fram'	£40
Aus Nansen in Nacht und Eis/Set 12/	
Meissner & Buch/Series 1016	£15

1897 Andree (Sweden)
Hot Air Balloon
Set 25/Bergeret, Nancy	£60
Portraits etc/1930 discovery	£15

1899 'Princesse Alice'
Prince Albert of Monaco etc in Spitzbergen / set 24	£30

1899 Abruzzi /Cagni (Italy)
On board the `Stella Polare'	£50
Rome Conference 1901/	
Subscription Cards	£40
Various cards	£35

1901 Otto Sverdrup
Various cards	£40

1903-1905 Ziegler/`America'
Various cards	£40

Captain Buchanan R/P £6

Colonel Flatters , Sahara £20

1903 Swedish South Polar Expedition
'SY Antarctic' Expedition views / set 12	£60
Argentine rescue pub La Nacion / 16	£40
Various Argentine rescue	£50

1908 Robert Peary (USA)
N.Pole Gravure /Hampton's mag/ set 13	£10
Kawin & Co./Chicago/Set 50/bw photos	£8
Taggart/Series of sepia photos	£6
Tuck R. & Sons/Oilettes/Operati A.	£6
Ullman North Pole Series 162/Wall B.	£6
S.S. `Roosevelt'/Inset Peary portrait/	
Set 3 Official/p.u. 12.9.09	£75
Peary & Cook/Comic sketches	£5

1911 Filchner (Germany)
Views of 'Deutschland', various	£50

Hot Air Balloon/`Princess Alice'
Set 24/Alfonso XIII & Prince of Monaco etc. in Spitzberg	£30

1925-26 North Pole flights in Airships/ Dirigibles by Amundsen, Bennett, Byrne, Ellsworth, Nobile
Various cards	£30

1934 J.B. Charcot (France)
Shipwreck 1936	£35
Funeral 1936	£60

1936 J.B.Charcot (France)
Shipwreck 1936	£35
Funeral 1936	£60
1954 Australian Antarctic Bases	
Pub. Seven Seas stamps / set 5	£8
1957 Trans-Antarctic Expedition	
bw photos / set 7	£8

EVEREST
1922 Expedition
Group photo/RP	£15

1924 Expedition
p.u. from Rongbuk Base Camp	£20

SAHARA
1921 Capt. Angus Buchanan
Set 12/Portraits & Events R/P	£6

GLAMOUR

One of the stalwarts of the Edwardian picture postcard industry as shown by the great numbers handed down to us. Glamour cards in one form or another are to be found in almost every original album, although the top of the range Artists and photographic Nudes are none too common. These were to be collected mainly in France, or by our troops during the First World War.

Market Report
There is always demand for top quality material. Anything less than perfect condition needs to go in the bargain boxes!

ART STUDIES
Chromo-Litho

Meissner & Buch	£15
Other publishers	£10

Nudes/Semi-Nudes

Pin-up type	£6
French Salon/Coloured	£4
/Sepia/BW	£2
Classical Art	£1

Pretty Girls

Better cards/Pre-1914	£3
Miscellaneous	£1.50

USA Post-War Pin-Ups

Machine cards/Plain back	£5

Mutoscope by
Carl Moran
£5

BATHING BEAUTIES
Embossed/Artist drawn

Chromo-Litho	£10
Other types	£5

Photographic/Portraits

Miscellaneous	£3

PHOTOGRAPHIC
Nudes
Prices given both for Nudes and Lingerie apply equally to plain back cards as these formed the bulk of publishers' output during this period.

France c.1916/RP	£15
Germany/Italy etc.c.1916/RP	£12
c.1916/Coloured/Hand Tinted	£18
Printed/Bw & Sepia	£6
Stage Acts/The Seldoms	£8
Couples	£8
Between the Wars	£6
Post-War studies	£3
Body Stocking types	£4
Private photographs	£2
Modern reproductions	£1.50

SM Interest

Numbered RP series c.1920	£20
Bondage/Spanking etc.	£15

Lingerie Studies	£10

Pretty Girls

Better cards/Pre-1914	£3
Miscellaneous	£1

MISCELLANEOUS
Pornographic/Postcard back

Art/Photographic	£18

Plain back cards have no commercial value otherthan curiosity appeal.

Lesbian interest	£18

Erotica

Photographic	£18
Art	£6
Comic Sketches	£6

Bedroom Scenes

Art/Photographic	£4

Miss Europe Competition

RP studies of contestants	£3

Maurice Miliere £15

A. Penot £15

M. Marco £4

Real Photographic hand tinted £15

GLAMOUR

Real Photographic SM Interest £20

I'm in for a good time!   Ayant peur de mouiller son costume.

W. Barribal £12

Black and White Printed £6

W.R.Ellam embossed chromo litho £10

GREETINGS

Greetings Cards in one form or another provided the bulk of the Edwardian publishers' output. Birthday and Christmas cards of all types were produced in their millions, while the better Embossed cards remain as superb examples of the printer's art. Coin and Stamp Cards were published in long series, although these have never been too popular in today's market. Other themes have been grouped together to make this heading.

Market Report

For the quality of some of the cards in this category, prices are ridiculously low. Halloween and better multi-babies are worth looking out for but there is little demand for much else.

COIN CARDS

National Coinage

Embossed	£8
Printed	£5

Banknote Cards

Embossed	£8
Printed	£5

DATE CARDS

Turn of the Century/Postally used

Sent 31.12.99/Received 1.1.00	£30

Year Dates/Up to 1903

Embossed	£10
Printed	£3

Year Dates/1904 onwards

Embossed	£6
Printed	£4

Calendar Cards £4

EMBOSSED

Grade A	£12
Grade B	£5
Grade C	£1

These are as difficult to describe as they are to illustrate! At the top of the range are the superb chromo-litho cards of ornate design, in the middle are the great bulk of nice Embossed, while below these come the common, run of the mill types.

FANTASY

Enlarged Objects	£4
Erotic	£12
Faces in Smoke etc.	£4
Fantasy Maps	£15
Multi-Babies	£3

Fantasy Heads

Coloured	£25
Black & White	£10

Faces in Mountains

Pub. Killinger	£12
Later issues	£4

Many Happy Returns

Embossed Greeting £5

National Coinage £8

FATHER CHRISTMAS

Hold to Light type	£85
WWI Silk type	£20
Tuck Oilette	£8
Coloured	£6
Photo type	£3
Snowmen	£3

Early embossed

Red robes	£15
Other Coloured Robes	£16

Prices are for good full-length or full-face Santas. Small designs or those with Santa forming part of a larger picture are worth less.

LANGUAGE

Deaf and Dumb Alphabet	£5
Language of Fruit	£2
Language of Stamps	£2
Language of Vegetables	£2

Esperanto

Tuck R. & Sons/Oilette series	£8
Miscellaneous issues	£3/£5

Language of Flowers

Welch J & Sons	£1.50
Miscellaneous issues	£1.50

Thanksgiving Day, £3

RECREATIONAL

Casinos	£1.50
Playing Cards	£8
Roulette Wheel Cards	£2

Romance

Cupid's Darts/Welch J. & Sons	£1.50
Proverbs/Welch J. & Sons	£1.50
Miscellaneous Comic Types	£1.50
Greetings/Sentimental/Lovers	£1

LARGE LETTER

Names of People	£2
Names of Places	£2
Numbers	£2-£4

Cherubs

Tuck R. & Sons	£12
Other series Embossed	£8
Printed	£4

Initials

Colour embossed	£8
Coloured	£4
B/W & Sepia	£2

Fifth Birthday, £4

SEASONAL GREETINGS

Christmas	£1
Decoration Day	£6
Easter	£1
Halloween	£8
Independence Day	£4
New Year	£1
Poisson d'Avril	£1
St. Patrick's Day	£3
Thanksgiving Day	£3
Valentine's Day	£5

These are prices representing the average card found in any section, but the spectacular item will fetch considerably more.

Birthday

Deckle-edge c.1930	.50
Miscellaneous	£1

STAMP CARDS

Embossed	£8
Printed	£5

Certain countries, e.g. Canada, realise a considerable premium.

MISCELLANEOUS

Champagne Bottles	£5
Davis Message Cards	£1.50
Fireworks	£6
Flowers	£1
Fruit	£1
Hands Across the Sea	£1.50
Moonlight	£1
Mottos/Sayings	£1
Rough Seas	£1
Swastikas/Greetings type	£1

Faith, Hope and Charity

Set 3	£5
Single cards	£1.50

Silhouettes

Camp Silhouette Series/ 25 cards/Photochrom Co.	£3
Cut-out types	£6
Printed types	£2

Smoking

Cigarette Card Comics	£20
Cigarettes/Pipes/Tobacco	£4

Miscellaneous Greetings

Better cards/Pre-1914	£3
General Types	£1

With the lower value Greetings cards, Christmas and Birthday etc., anything Embossed, or printed Chromo-Litho, or carrying an unusual design, would certainly be worth more.

Christmas Greetings Embossed £10

Happy Christmas with cut outs £12

HERALDIC

Originally far more popular than they are now, Heraldic cards of all kinds were published in profusion by the Edwardians. Perhaps the sense of identity with a particular town or city was stronger then than it is now, certainly this would account for the enormous numbers of cards left to us.

Market Report
The market is over supplied with unsaleable cards. Early map cards are the only bright spot here.

FULL OUT CRESTS

Faulkner C.W. & Co.	£3
Ja-Ja- Heraldic Series	
Stoddart & Co.	£2
School/University Arms	
Robert Peel Postcard Co	£1.50
Reliable Series	
W. Ritchie & Sons	£1.50
Multi-crest cards	£1
Special Crests	
Sports/Occupations	£1.50
Miscellaneous Publishers	
Better cards/Pre-1914	£2
General issues	£1

CRESTS WITH VIEWS

B & R's Camera Series	
Brown & Rawcliffe	£1.50
Faulkner C.W. & Co.	
Cathedrals/Stately Homes	£1.50
Favourite Series	
W.E. Byers	£1
F.S.O. Heraldic Series	£2
Ja-Ja- Heraldic Series	
Stoddart & Co.	£3
Jarrold's Series	£1
Robert Peel Postcard Co.	£1.50
Reliable Series	
W. Ritchie & Sons	£1
Tuck R. & Sons	
Heraldic Series	£12
Heraldic View	£2
Valentine's Series	£1
Miscellaneous Publishers	£1

MISCELLANEOUS

Papal Series	
Ferloni L.	£5
FLAGS/NATIONAL ARMS	
Aristophot Flag Series	£1.50
E.F.A. Series	
Excelsior Fine Art	£1.50
Faulkner C.W. & Co.	
Early series	£6
Arms of the Nations	
Kohl/Tuck R. & Sons	£12
Flags of the Nations	
Valentine & Sons	£4

Miscellaneous Publishers	
Embossed/Chromo-Litho	£8
Printed/Coloured	£1.50

TARTANS

B.B.	
Tartan View Series	£1
Brown & Rawcliffe	
Arms, Views & Tartans	£1
B & R's Camera Series	£1
Cynicus Co.	£1
Johnston W. & A.K.	
Tartan & Arms Series	£3
Stoddart & Co./Ja-Ja	
Clan Tartan Heraldic Series	£3
Tuck R. & Sons	
Scottish Clans Series	£3
Valentine & Sons	
Tartan Series	£1.50
Valentine's Series	£1
Wildt & Kray	
Badge & Tartan	£2
Miscellaneous types	£1

MAP CARDS

Early Chromo /Embossed	£6/ £25
Mountain Charts	£1
Romantic/Comic types	£1
Walker John & Co.	
Geographical Series	£8

South America Map Card. £8

LITERARY/MUSIC

Judging from the diverse range and numbers remaining, cards of Literary and Musical interest would appear to have been quite popular in the pre-television days of our forebears. A good subject to collect, reflecting as it does, a wide spread of artistic endeavour.

Market Report
There is a fairly refined audience for musicians and opera stars. The literary world has little to say for itself at present.

DICKENS

Cassell & Co./Barnard F.
Character Sketches from Dickens   £4

Chapman & Hall
Dickens Novels/Set 13   £6

Faulkner & Co.
Pickwick Series/244   £4

Hildesheimer/Manning E.F.
Dickens Characters   £4

Jones A.V.N./Reynolds F.
Dickens Characters   £5

Stewart & Woolf/Crowquill A.
Dickens Characters/3 sets   £4

Tuck R. & Sons
Early Numbered Series   £12
Dickens Postcard Series/Kyd   £12
Dombey and Son/
Set 6/Oilette 6050   £3
Nicholas Nickleby/
Set 6/Oilette 6052   £3
With Famous Authors & Painters   £4
In Dickens' Land/Oilettes   £2
Dickens Characters   £4

Valentine
Dickens Characters   £4

Portraits/Sites/Events   £1.50

MISCELLANEOUS

Alice in Wonderland
Nixon K./Set 6/
Faulkner & Co./Series 1819   £12
Tenniel/Set 8/
Fuller & Richard   £12
Folkard C./Set 6/
A&C Black/Series 80   £12

Literary Personalities
Early Chromos   £8
Later Portraits   £1.50

Lorna Doone
Scenes from Lorna Doone/
Set 12/Photochrom Co.   £1.50
Characters from Lorna Doone/
Valentine   £1.50

Early Tuck, Thomas Hardy £12

Poetry
Patience Strong cards   £1
Verses/Miscellaneous   £1

Sherlock Holmes   £10

SHAKESPEARE

Ackermann/Munich
Silhouettes/Set 12   £5

Faulkner & Co.
Shakespeare Series   £5

Hildesheimer/Carter S.
Sketches from Shakespeare   £2

Nister E.
Scenes from Shakespeare/ub   £8
Later series/Divided back   £2

Tuck R. & Sons
Early Numbered Series   £12
Hamlet/Set 12/Copping H.   £5
Merry Wives of Windsor/
Series 466-477   £5
In Shakespeare's Country/Oilettes   £2

Valentine
Characters from Shakespeare   £2

Portraits/Sites/Events   £1

BANDS

Brass Bands	£6
Dance Bands	£10
Military Bands	£6
Pipe Bands	£5
Dagenham Girl Pipers	£3
Champion Bandsmen	£4
Band Leaders	£5

OPERA

Gilbert & Sullivan

Savoy Co.	£12
Other Publishers	£8

Breitkoff & Hartel/Set 60

Wagner Series	£12

Faulkner & Co./Series 1401

Wagners Operas/Set 12	£15

Meissner & Buch

Wagner series	£18

Ricordi

Chromo-litho ub/Japanese style	£18
Madame Butterfly	£18
Tosca	£18

Tuck R. & Sons

Wagner series	£18
Opera Houses	£5

Opera Singers

Butt Clara	£5
Caruso Enrico	£20
Chaliapin	£20
Melba Dame Nellie	£10
Patti Adeline	£10
Tetrazzini	£10
Other Singers	£6

POP STARS

Beatles	£7.50
Others 1960's/70's	£3+
Modern	.50
Elvis	£9

SONG CARDS
BAMFORTH

Set 3	£4.50
Set 4	£6

Prices are for complete sets

Odd cards	£1.50

OTHER TYPES

Miscellaneous Types	£1

Tuck R. & Sons

Illustrated Songs Series	£1.50

'Tuck's' Men of Letters £5

MISCELLANEOUS

Bandstands	£5
Bells	£1.50
Bellringers	£8
Hymns	£1
Musical Instruments	£3
Advertised by musicians	£6
Musicians	£3
Orchestras	£6
Singers	£3

Composers

Art Studies	£3
Photographic	£2

Gramophones

Art/Photographic	£8
Comic types	£5

Jazz

Bands/Groups	£12
Instrumentalists/Singers	£12

Organs

Church	£2
Cinema/Theatre	£5

Song Cards/Musical Notation

Embossed	£5
Printed	£1.50

MILITARY

The Military conflicts of history from the Boer War to the present day have always been covered by the picture postcard. In a variety of styles ranging from actual battle scenes to the personalities, patriotic and propaganda issues of the period, the postcard was not slow to reflect current tastes and national sentiment. The many issues relating to the First World War form the largest catalogue.

Market Report

Photographic camps, transport and regimental portraits are all in demand. Boer War, Gale and Polden and artist drawn cards generally seem to be in retreat. Expect a pick up in interest in the First World War as we approach the centenary.

For Political Cartoons in all sections please see POLITICAL classification.

SPANISH AMERICAN WAR 1898
Miscellaneous types	£25

BOER WAR 1899-1902
Jamestown Raid	£40
St. Helena/Camps etc.	£25
War Photographs	£15
Sites & Events/Historic	£5

City Press
C.I.V./bw Vignettes	£15

Collectors Publishing Co.
Personalities/Photographic	£15

Koumans P.J.
Personalities/Photographic	£15

Picture Postcard Co.
War Sketches/Caton Woodville etc.	£20
Personalities/Vignettes	£20

Tuck R. & Sons
Peace Card/Coloured Vignette	£25
Souvenir of 1900	£25
Empire Series/Art Sketches/bw	£18
Overprinted for Victories	£30

Other Publishers
Early Vignettes/Coloured	£18
Early Vignettes/bw	£15

BOXER REBELLION 1900-1901

The Boxer Rebellion was an uprising by members of the Chinese Society of Right and Harmonious Fists against foreign influence in areas such as trade, politics, religion and technology. The campaigns took place from November 1899 to 7 September 1901, during the final years of Manchu rule in China under the Qing Dynasty.
The members of the Society of Right and Harmonious Fists were simply called "Boxers" by the Westerners due to the martial arts and callisthenics they practised.

War Photographs	£25
Caricature	£40-45
Publishers include Eysler, Bruno Burger, Kunzli freres	

Troops, ships and railways	£20
Publishers include Franz Scholz, E.Lee, Brun et cie (Expedition de Chine).	
Notable artist Willy Stower (ships)	

Villages,towns,forts etc	£15
publishers as below, Max Wolff.	

Below; Boxer Rebellion, Fort £15

Tsingtau-Kiautschou

Ostlager

Above; Boxer Rebellion Caricature *£40*

RUSSO-JAPANESE WAR 1904-1905
Military Review 1906
With Kobe Handstamp	£10
With Tokyo Handstamp	£8
Without Handstamp	£6

Japanese Official
Post Office 1904 issue	£8
Photo montage/Art Borders	£8
Communications Dept/Post War issue	£5

Peace Conference
Knight Bros./Multi-view	£8
Miscellaneous issues	£5

Below; Boxer Rebellion Troops,
(Expedition de Chine) *£20*

*National War Bond tank in Trafalgar Square
Printed photo type £6*

Russian Outrage on Hull Fleet
Real Photographic	£5
Valentines/Other Publishers	£3

Tuck R. & Sons
Real Photographic Series 5170	£8
Russo-Japanese Series 1330	£8
Russo Japanese War Photographs/	
Set 6/Silverette 6534	£8
The Russo-Japanese War/	
Set 6/Oilette 6484	£6

WarPhotographs/Sketches
Hildesheimer/War Series 5224	£6
Other Publishers	£5

ITALIAN-TURKISH WAR 1911-1912
War Photographs
Traldi/Milan	£12
Miscellaneous issues	£8

CHINESE CIVIL WAR 1911-1917
War Photographs	£15
Art Studies	£8

BALKAN WARS 1912-1913
War Photographs	£12

WORLD WAR 1 1914-1918
FUND RAISING CARDS
Anglo-Russian Hospital Fund	£3
Asiles de Soldats Invalides Belges	£2
Belgian Relief Funds	£3
Bovril/Lord Roberts	£5
British Ambulance Committee	£3
British Committee of the	
French Red Cross	£3
British Gifts for Belgian Soldiers	£3
National Egg Fund	£5
National Fund for Welsh Troops	£2
National Institute for the Blind	£1.50
National Relief Fund	£3
Performer Tobacco Fund	£6

Red Cross	£4
War Bond Campaign/Set 12	£3
Y.M.C.A. Hut Fund	£4

National War Bond Tank
Trafalgar Square	£6
In G.B. locations	£18

War Bond Campaign Postcard
Trafalgar Square	£5
In G.B. locations	£15

Weekly Dispatch Tobacco Fund
`Arf a Mo' Kaiser/Thomas B.	£4

War Loan/Patriotic Designs
France	£5
Germany	£6
Italy	£5
Russia	£8

NAVAL ACTIONS
Bombardment of Britain 1914	£12

Scapa Flow
German Fleet/Sinking etc.	£8

Zeebrugge
WW1 Actions/Interest	£1

OFFICIAL STATIONARY/ FIELD SERVICE CARDS
Great Britain	£2
France	£2
Germany	£3
Other Countries	£3

PATRIOTIC
Admirals of the British Navy
Francis Dod	£3

Britain Prepared Series
24 cards/Photochrom Co.	£3

Butterfly Girls
Published Geligne/Marotte	£8

Generals of the British Army
Francis Dodd	£3

Heroes of the War
Cuneo, Cyrus	£10

Leurs Caboches/Nos Allies/Nos Poilus
Dupuis Emile	£5
Les Femmes Heroiques	
Dupuis Emile	£5

Out for Victory
Hill L. Raven-	£4

Series 1021
Vivien Mansell	£4

The Allies Series
James Henderson	£4

Morant Military Hospital, this is a good photographic card and is easily worth £12

United Six Series
Inter-Art Co.	£4

Types
Bulldogs	£6
Comic	£3
Flags	£3
Poems	£1.50
Royalty	£3

Miscellaneous Types
Great Britain	£3
France	£3
Germany	£6
Other Countries	£3

PERIOD SENTIMENT
Great Britain	£1.50
France	£1.50
Germany	£2
Other Countries	£2

PERSONALITIES
France	£2
Other Countries	£3

Germany
Generals/RP Portraits	£8
Art Studies	£5
Other Generals/Leaders	£3

Great Britain
Kitchener Memorial Card	£3
Other Generals/Leaders	£1.50

PRISONERS OF WAR
Allied in German Camps
Art sketches	£10
Photographic	£5

German in Allied Camps
Photographic	£6

WELFARE ORGANISATIONS
Church Army	£3
Salvation Army	£3
St. Dunstans	£3
Y.M.C.A.	£3

Red Cross
There are many cards issued by Red Cross Organisations dealing with aspects of WW1 in their respective countries,
A guide to price may be inferred by reference to similar themes in the WW1 section and a premium added for the presence of the Red Cross symbol. We woud suggest £5 as a basic price.

WAR PHOTOGRAPHS
Chicago Daily News	£4
E.L.D/N.D. etc.	£4
Hildesheimer & Co.	£4
Imperial War Museum	£2
In the Balkans/E.L.D.	£3
L.V. Cie	£3
Official Photograph/Censored at GHQ	£3
Photochrom Co.	
Bw series	£4
On Active Service/Set 48	£3
Sketch The	£4
Sphere The	£4
French Edition	£4
Sport & General Press Agency	£3
Tit-Bits	£3
War Photogravure Publications	£3
The War Series	£3
World War Series	£3
Yes or No	£3
Special Cards	£5

Daily Mail Battle Pictures
Numbers 1 - 96	£2
Numbers 97-144	£2.50
Numbers 145-160/Anzac Series	£6
Numbers 161-176	£4

This famous series was published in 22 sets of 8 cards each.

Photographic card showing British Artillery during practice WW1 £8

Daily Mail War postcards, showing men loading a trench mortar £3

Real Photographic series	£6

Daily Mirror
Canadian Official Series/RP	£5
Coloured	£3
Sepia	£3

Newspaper Illustrations £3
Black & White series	£3
Coloured series	£3
Sepia series	£3
Shell damage Series	£1

Regent Publishing Co.
The War Series	£3

Tuck R. & Sons
At the Front	£4
The European War 1914	£3
Types of Allied Armies	£4

Miscellaneous
Great Britain	£3
France	£3
Germany	£5
Other Countries	£5

MISCELLANEOUS WORLD WAR 1
Allied Occupation/Germany 1919	£4
Armoured Cars	£6
Campaign Maps	£5
Cemeteries/Memorials	£1.50
Conscientious Objectors	£20
German proclamations issued in French towns	£4
Greetings Cards/Regimental	£6
Mesopotamia Campaign	£4
Palestine Campaign	£8
Recruiting Parades/Departures	£25
Refugees in G.B.	£25
Salonika Campaign	£3
Shell Damage/Foreign	£1
Tanks	£4

Christmas Cards
From POW Camps	£8

Miscellaneous	£3

Dardanelles Campaign
Gallipoli/Anzac Cove/Suvla Bay etc.
Troops/Action	£12
RP Landscapes	£6

Dogs
Major Richardson's War Dogs	£8
Red Cross War Dogs	£8

Victory Parades
GB	£1.50
Paris 1919	£1.50

War Wounded
Brighton	£6
Miscellaneous	£3

Women on War Work
For the Cause/Tuck R. & Sons	£8
La Femme et La Guerre/Leroy	£8
Our Own Girls/Arthur Butchur	£8
Miscellaneous	£8

There are many other photographic cards, particularly those issued by Germany, France and Belgium depicting different aspects of World War 1,
Good quality photographic cards showing British women in uniform and carrying out war work are sought after.

RUSSIAN CIVIL WAR 1917-1921
Allied Expeditionary Forces	£15
Red Propaganda	£18
White Russian Propaganda	£20
Miscellaneous Issues	£10

GRAECO-TURKISH WAR 1919-1923
War Photographs
Smyrna	£15
Miscellaneous issues	£8

WW1 Women at war, Motorcycle messengers or postal workers £15

SPANISH CIVIL WAR 1936-1939

Gen. Franco	£15
Republican Propaganda	£20
War Photographs	£20
Military Personalities	£15

ITALIAN-ABYSSINIAN WAR 1938

War Photographs	£12

WORLD WAR 2/1939-1945

OFFICIAL STATIONERY/FIELD SERVICE CARDS

Germany	£3
U.S.A.	£3
Other Countries	£2

PATRIOTIC

Great Britain	£8
France	£5
Germany	£12
Netherlands	£5
U.S.A.	£8

PERSONALITIES

France	£4
Germany	£10
U.S.A.	£4
Gen. Eisenhower	£5
Other Countries	£4

This superb poster advert for Red Cross, published during the spanish civil war £40

YEAH, MOM, I'M DOING SWELL — I'VE TAKEN ON ABOUT FORTY POUNDS

WW2 Comic, USA published card to promote war bonds, these are collected at £5

Great Britain

Churchill	£4/£8
Gen. Montgomery	£5
Other Leaders	£3

WAR PHOTOGRAPHS/SKETCHES
Photochrom Co.

Britain Prepared	£3

Salmon

Aviation sketches/A.F.D. Bannister	£5

Valentine

Real Photograph series/Aviation	£2
Aircraft Recognition silhouettes	£2

MISCELLANEOUS WORLD WAR 2

Prisoners of War	£10
Tanks/Guns/Vehicles	£5
V2 Rocket on display	£8
With The W.A.A.F./Set 24	
Sepia photos/Tuck R. & Sons	£20
Women on War Work	£12

Comic Sketches

Bizeth/Sets of 6/Price per set	£36
Dutch Troops	£4
U.S.A.Troops	£4
Maneken-Pis	£3
Tuck R. & Sons	£4

Germany

Erich Gutjahr Series	£8

This is an extensive numbered series of superb RP studies of the Germany Army in WW2.

Germany/6x4 size

Generals/RP Portraits	£12
Patriotic Posters	£12
Hitler/Portraits	£12
Luftwaffe propaganda	£10

Peace Celebrations
Amsterdam Victory Parade 1945

6x4 size	£5
VE Day	£6
VJ Day	£6

Red Cross

As with WW1 there were many cards issued by Red Cross Organisations in WW2 dealing with aspects of war In their respective countries.A guide to price may be inferred by reference to similar themes in the WW2 section and a premium added for the presence of the Red Cross symbol. We would suggest £5 as a basic price.

Shell Damage

London Blitz	£4
Foreign	£1.50

USA

Troops/Action	£5
Pre-war Camp Life	£3

There are many photographic cards, particularly those issued by Germany, France and Belgium depicting different aspects of World War 2, including Troops in Action, At Rest, Anti-Aircraft emplacements, Ammunition Transport, Convoys, Gun Crews, Machine Gun Nests,Vehicles etc. One may use a guide price of around £5 for such cards, bearing in mind that some will be worth more, some less

Gale & Polden published coloured military cards, similar to this, would sell for £6

MILITARY ART

Gale & Polden

History & Traditions	£10
History & Traditions/Rates of Pay	£18
Regimental Badges	£6
Miscellaneous Coloured	£6

Knight Bros.	£3

Lavauzelle C./Paris

Early Vignettes	£8

Valentine

The Kings Army	£3

Italian Regimental

Chromo-Litho	£12
Sepia/Black & White	£4

Miscellaneous Art/Coloured

Early Vignettes	£12
Later Issues	£3

Photographic Studies

Coloured	£3
Black & White	£1.50

Tuck R. & Sons

Oilette Series

3100 Cavalry on Active Service/ Harry Payne	£18
3105 Our Fighting Regiments/ The RoyalArtillery/Harry Payne	£12
3113 Comrades/ Harry Payne	£25
3159 The US Army on the Western Front /Harry Payne	£25
3160 Colonial Badges and their Wearers/ Harry Payne	£15
3163 Our Fighting Regiments/ 1st LifeGuards/Harry Payne	£15
3165 Our Fighting Regiments/ 1st Dragoon Guards/Harry Payne	£15
3204 Badges and their Wearers/ Harry Payne	£75
3205 Badges and their Wearers/ Harry Payne	£75
3546 Military in London/ Harry Payne	£5
3642 Scots Pipers/ Harry Payne	£8
6412 Military in London/ Harry Payne	£4
8491 Badges and their Wearers/ Harry Payne	£50
8625 The Scots Guards/ Harry Payne	£12
8635 The 21st Lancers/ Harry Payne	£12
8637 17th Lancers/ Harry Payne	£15
8731 Our Territorials/ Harry Payne	£12
8732 Wake up England/ Harry Payne	£15
8738 Types of the British Army	£30
8761 Defenders of the Empire/ Harry Payne	£12
8762 The Red Cross Series/ Harry Payne	£30
8763 The Royal Horse Artillery/ Harry Payne	£12
8770 Regimental Bands/	

Harry Payne	£5	**British in India**	
8807 16th Lancers/		Military Life/Sites etc.	£4
Harry Payne	£15		
8831 1st Royal Dragoons/		**Italian Regimental**	
Harry Payne	£15	Menus/Patriotic/Seals etc.	£4
8835 1st Life Guards/		Chromo-Litho designs	£12
Harry Payne	£15		

British in India
Military Life/Sites etc. £4

Italian Regimental
Menus/Patriotic/Seals etc. £4
Chromo-Litho designs £12

Harry Payne £5
8807 16th Lancers/
Harry Payne £15
8831 1st Royal Dragoons/
Harry Payne £15
8835 1st Life Guards/
Harry Payne £15
8848 11th Hussars/
Harry Payne £15
8871 Badges and their Wearers/
Harry Payne £15
8890 6th Dragoon Guards/
Harry Payne £10
9081 Military in London II/
Harry Payne £5
9132 Deeds of British Heroism £8
9134 British Battles £8
9139 Military Life & Military Tournaments/
Harry Payne £5
9478 The British Army £5
9527 Life at Aldershot/
Harry Payne £15
9587 Military in London III/
Harry Payne £5
9762 Scotch Pipers/
Harry Payne £8
9883 Queens Own Cameron Highlanders/
Harry Payne £12
9884 Gordon Highlanders/
Harry Payne £12
9885 Seaforth Highlanders/
Harry Payne £12
9934 For Home and Empire/
Harry Payne £15
9937 Argyll and Sutherland Highlanders/
Harry Payne £12
9980 Royal Scots Greys/
Harry Payne £12
9993 Coldstream Guards/
Harry Payne £12
9994 Black Watch/
Harry Payne £12

Life in the Army
Gale & Polden £3
Star Series £1.50
Miscellaneous photographs £3

Medals
Present Day War Ribbons/Rees H. £4
V.C. Winners/Various issues £10
Daring Deeds £3

Military Tattoos/Displays
Aldershot £1.50
Royal Tournament £1.50
Miscellaneous Events £1.50

Uniforms/Dress
Mrs. Albert Broom series/Guardsmen £8
Regimental photographs £3
Identified £3
Unidentified £1.50

Unknown Warrior
Cenotaph Services/Parades £2

There are many photographic cards depicting aspects of pre-war Military Life in different countries, including Troops on exercise, Parades, Training etc. One may use a guide price of around £3 for such cards, bearing in mind that some will be worth more, some less.

Tuck R. & Sons
Military in London/Oilettes £2
Unsigned Oilettes £3

MISCELLANEOUS
Artillery £2
Battlefields/Historic £1.50
Battle of Waterloo £1
Beefeaters £1
Joan of Arc £2
Napoleon £3

Army Camps
Field Camps/Named £8
Field Camps/Un-named £3
Hut Camps/Named £5
Hut Camps/Un-named £2
Barracks £5

Gale & Polden, Harry Payne £8

NAVAL

A vast and complex section where we will attempt to give some idea of the types of Warships in H. M.'s service.

Publishers produced large quantities of cards relating to capital ships where crews often numbered 1000-1200+. These are common and so priced. Other R/P's of named ships in exotic ports and harbours are of more interest and priced according to location.

Market Report:
There is strong demand from the family history lobby. Hospital ships are popular as are ships in exotic locations. Nelson is still afloat but naval life isn't all it could be.

Tuck's 'Our Ironclads', HMS Russell £5

Meissner & Buch, Series 1000 Battleships & Cruisers, by Hans Bohrdt £20

BATTLESHIPS/CRUISERS

Tuck R. & Sons	
Empire Series	£20
Oilette Series	£3/5
Artist drawn	£3/5

Foreign Types	
Early Vignettes	£15
Visit of US Fleet to Melbourne	
1908 / Embossed / Inset Ship	£18
Japanese Official/Inset Ship	£10/15
Pre - 1939	£3/10
1939 Onwards	£3/5

LIFE IN THE NAVY

Gale & Polden	£2/4
Nelson Victory Cards	£2/5

Miscellaneous	
Shotley Barracks/HMS Ganges	£4
Ships moored off-shore	£4
Other Barracks etc.	£4
Wooden Walls (Training Ships)	£4-10
Fleet Reviews/Displays	£3
Naval Engagements/Sketches	£6/£8
Personalities	£2
Sailor's Photographs etc.	£2
Graf Spee sinking set of 12	£6

Ships Cat, HMS Algerine, Vengeance, Barfleur, Renown. R/P £6

HMS 'Lord Nelson', R/P £4

The Imperial British Navy

Battleships	£4
Dreadnought Cruisers	£4
Battlecruisers	£3/5
Cruisers	£4
Aircraft Carriers	£5/8
Sea Plane Carriers	£6-10
Flotilla Leaders	£3/4
Destroyers	£3/4
Torpedo Boat Destroyers	£4
Submarines	£4/6
Sloops	£5/6
Mine Layers	£5
Mine Sweepers	£5

Small Craft & Auxiliaries

River Gunboats	£8+
Monitors	£6+
Patrol Boats	£5
Motor Torpedo Boats	£3/5
Depot Ships	£4/£6
Repair Ships	£5
Hospital Ships	£12/16
Surveying Ships	£5
Yachts.	£3/6
1939-1950 R/Ps	£2/5

Others Include :-

Drifters	£6
Ice Breakers	£7
Target Ships	£3
Troopships	£ 4 / 6
Tugs	£3

HMS 'Argyll' Heavy Cruiser R/P

HMS 'Natal' Heavy Cruiser R/P

HMS 'Falmouth' Light Cruiser R/P

HMS 'Nottingham' Light Cruiser R/P

All sunk or wrecked between 1915-1918

HMS 'Cochrane' Heavy Cruiser R/P

Battleship "Rodney" *R/P* *£4*

Flotilla Leader "Keith" - Sunk 1940 R/P £6

Battlecruiser "Hood" R/P *£5*

Destroyer "Ambuscade" R/P *£3*

Cruiser "Gloucester" *R/P* *£4*

Submarine "E9" *R/P* *£6*

Aircraft Carrier "Hermes" *R/P* *£6*

Sloop "Dwarf" *R/P* *£6*

Minesweeper "Harebell"   R/P   £5

Depot Ship "Titania"   R/P   £6

Monitor and Destroyers   R/P   £8

Repair Ship "Assistance"   R/P   £4

Patrol boat "P.40"   R/P   £4

Hospital Ship   "St.George" R/P   £15

Motor Torpedo Boat   R/P   £4

Surveying Ship "Flinders"   R/P   £4

NOVELTY

Today, as in the past, a strong collecting area, where the original publishers vied with each other to produce the exotic and unusual cards which now make up this category. Novelty cards are those which do something, or have things attached to them, or which deviate in any way from the norm.

Market Report

This section is regarded with something akin to horror by most dealers. Cards that squeak, levers that get damaged, hold to light cards you can't see through - collectors aren't impressed much either. Bookmarks, stamp montages and pull out town views are steady sellers though.

APPLIQUED MATERIALS

Dried Flowers	£2
Feathered Birds	£10
Feathered Hats	£6
Glass Eyes	£5
Glitter Cards	£1.50
Jewellery	£3
Lace	£6
Matchbox Strikers	£12
Material	£2
Metal Models	£10
Mirror Cards	£2
Photo Inserts	£1.50
Real Hair	£10
Sand Pictures	£4
Seeds	£2

HOLD TO LIGHT

Exhibitions	£15
Father Christmas	£85
Flames	£18
Gruss Aus type	£12
Greetings/Churches etc.	£6
G.B. Views/W.H. Berlin	£4
Large Letter/Date cards	£15
Better Designs	£15

Real Hair
£10

Mechanical Kaleidoscope £30

COMPOSITE SETS

Animals/Set 3/5	£30/£50
G.P. Government Tea/Set 6	£120
Jeanne d'Arc/Set 10/12	£75
Jesus Christ/Set 10/12	£75
Nansen/Set 4	£400
Napoleon/Set 10/12	£75
Samurai Warriors/Set 8/10/12	£96/£144

Albert Memorial/Set 15

F.G.O. Stuart	£60

Map of London/Set 6

Tuck R. & Sons/Series 9352	£75

MATERIALS

Aluminium	£3
Celluloid	£3
Leather	£3
Panel Cards	£1.50
Peat	£3
Rice Paper/Oolong Tea	£10
Wood	£3

Pull Out, Royal Mail Van £5

MECHANICAL

Blow Up	£20
Heat-activated	£6
Invisible Picture	£6
Kaleidoscopes	£30
Lever Change	£8
Moveable Hats	£5
Paper Chains	£15
Perfumed	£4
Push-Out Models	£20
Reversible Bottle/Sand etc.	£8
Squeakers	£5
Venetian Blinds	£6
Wagging Tails	£3

Cut-out Models

Tuck R. & Sons	£45+
Mack W.E./Henderson J.	£40
Star Series/Animals	£20
Later issues/Salmon J	£10

Gramophone Records

Ettlinger	£8
Tuck R. & Sons	£8
Other Publishers	£8

Jigsaw Puzzles

Tuck R. & Sons	£20
Other publishers	£12

Roller Blinds

Early type	£25
Later issues	£5

Rotating Wheels

Early type	£25
Later issues	£3

Stand-up Models

Exhibition types	£75

PULL OUTS

Animals	£3
Artist/signed	£5
Beer Bottles	£5
Buses	£6
Cats	£5
Comic	£3
Dogs	£5
Father Xmas	£10
Fortune Telling	£6
Hop-Picking	£8
Irish Subjects	£4
Mail Vans	£5
Military	£6
Motor Cars	£6
Postmen	£6
Railway Tickets named	£6
Shamrocks	£3
Teddy Bears	£12
Town views/multi-view fronts	£3
Trams	£8
Welsh Ladies	£3

SIZES

Folded	£3
Giant	£5
Midget	£3
Panorama	£5

Book Marks

Art type	£3
Actors/Actresses	£2
Egyptian Scenes	£1.50
Other types	£2

TRANSPARENCIES

Angels/Greetings	£6
Continental subjects	£10
Exhibitions	£15
Father Christmas	£12
GB Views/Hartmann	£8
GB Views	£3
Meteor	£10
Puzzle Type	£5

MISCELLANEOUS

Bas Relief	£3
Puzzle Cards	£4
Stamp Montage	£6

Shapes

Circular/Leaf etc.	£6

Three Dimensional

Pre-1914/With eye-piece	£6
Modern/Nudes etc.	£1

POLITICAL

This section covers a wide collecting field, reflecting perhaps a greater awareness of current affairs at the time. This is a major collecting area, covering Wars, Political satire and Social events, Campaigns and Strikes, etc. For more on this subject see our Military Section.

Market Report
Irish political and Spanish Civil war cards are outstripping catalogue prices. Churchill is universally admired but nobody seems to buy him! Suffragette comics are going down while events and personalities seem to be going back up!

Boer War, F.O'Beirne artist drawn card £15

CARTOONS/WAR
BOER WAR 1899-1902
Antiquariat Bremen	£18
Bruno Burger	£18
Friedello	£18
Kunzli Freres/Thiele A	£25
Regel & Krug	£18
Ropke & Woortman	£18
Vlieger J.G.	£18
Zieher Ottmar/Thiele A	£20
Leaders/Personalities	£15

BOXER REBELLION 1900-1901
Bruno Burger	£25
Kunzli Freres	£25

RUSSO-JAPANESE WAR 1904-1905
Hildesheimer/Hardy D	£15
P.L. Paris/Muller E.	£15
M.M. Paris	£1

WORLD WAR I/1914-1918
Great Britain
The Hun/E. Sachetti/ Set 6/Geo. Pulman & Sons.	£8
Davidson Bros./Ludovici A.	£5
Jarrold & Sons/Punch Cartoons	£3
Tuck R. & Sons/Aesop's Fables Set 6/Oilette 8484	£8
Miscellaneous Publishers	£4

France
Les Monstres des Cathedrales	£6
Miscellaneous Publishers	£4

Germany	£6
Italy	
Sculpture Montage types	£5
Miscellaneous Publishers	£5

Edith Cavell
Corbella T.	£10
Mourning Cards	£6
Portraits	£3
Grave	£2
See also Silk Cards	

Other Types
Human Butterflies/WWI Leaders	£10
Raemaekers, L	£4

OTHER CAMPAIGNS
Alsace Lorraine
Hansi	£15
Miscellaneous Cartoons	£5
Bulgaria 1903	£12

CARTOONS/SOCIAL
GREAT BRITAIN
Anti-Semitic	£20
National Insurance Acts	£4
Shops Act	£4
Worker's Compensation Acts	£5

Fiscal
Tuck R. & Sons/Game Birds	£8
Bradshaw P.V.	£8
Premier Series-The Fiscal policy	£8

Comic card to illustrate the new worker's compensation act £5

Tariff reform comic cards similar to this   £8

Masonic
Are You a Mason?
24 cards/Millar & Lang   £15

Tariff Reform
Free Trade/Family in Kitchen   £1
Other Types   £8

Other types
Westminster Cartoon Series   £6
Davidson Bros/Ludovici A.   £5
Faulkner & Co./Moreland A.   £6
Morning Leader Series   £6
Walker J. & Co./Furniss H.   £6
Wrench E./Punch Cartoons 1901   £8
Miscellaneous Publishers   £5

FRANCE
Anti-Royalty/KE VII Debauchery   £10
Russia/Czar Nicholas etc.   £15

Orens D./le Burin Satirique
& other Limited Edition Series   £15
ITALY
Fascist Cartoons   £12
Mussolini/Portraits   £10
/Hanging   £8

DREYFUS AFFAIR
Miscellaneous issues   £8
ELECTIONS
Candidates   £8
Canvassing Cards   £8
Poll Declarations   £10

Ulster Campaign, showing Sir Edward Carson. This also is a novelty pull-out with several pics of notable British supporters inside. Easily worth £25

IRISH HOME RULE
ULSTER CAMPAIGN
Sir Edward Carson/Portraits   £15
Meetings/U.V.F.   £25
Political Cartoons   £15/ £25

EIRE CAMPAIGN
Easter Rising 1916   £15
Gun Running   £75
Leaders   £35
Mourning Cards   £30
Troubles 1920   £25

Anti-Home Rule cartoon, posted 1906, £15

General Strike, May 1926 £25

WW2 Comic card by Midge £6

WORLD WAR 2/1939-1945 (ALLIES

All my own work by Grimes	£4
Anti-Nazi (Hitler Photo type)	£15
Bamforth Comic series	£5
ITMA comic	£5
Our Modern Army Reg Carter	£8
Miscellaneous Cartoons	£4/8
U.S. Armed forces	£4
'What a war' by G.Wilkinson	£4

WW2 Patriotic £6

Privately produced photographic postcard showing a a group of proud soldiers and their war trophy. Cards similar to this fetch around £8-12

NATIONAL SOCIALIST PARTY

Nationalist Socialist Party	£15
Hitler portraits	£15
Mosley period	£20

PERSONALITIES

Tuck R. & Sons/Empire Series	£20
Sir Winston Churchill	£6/15
Lloyd George	£4
Prime Ministers	£3/6
Cabinet Ministers	£3
Governor Generals	£3
M.P.'s Memorial Cards	£6
Foreign Personalities	£2 / £8
De Gaulle	£6
J.F.Kennedy	£6
Faulkner C.W./Series 41	
British Statesmen	£15

Great Britain	
Early Vignettes	£15
Portraits/Art	£3
Portraits/Photographic	£2
House of Commons/Lords	£1.50

POLITICAL EVENTS

Meetings/Treaties	£6
Mourning Cards	£6
Funerals	£6

Visits	
Czar Nicholas to France 1896	£25
Miscellaneous visits	£6

The photo shows a railway van which was overturned while conveying goods to our warehouse, during the great London Strike Aug. 10th. 1911.

NO TAXATION WITHOUT REPRESENTATION

1907 THE FRANCHISE WON ROLL OF HONOUR

"Go hang yourselves——We fought at Acre, and you were not there."

Printed and Published by the Artists' Suffrage League, 259 King's Road, Chelsea.

Suffragette cartoon, published by the Artist's Suffrage League £40

SUFFRAGETTE CAMPAIGN

Events/Demonstrations	£85
Leaders/Portraits	£70
Publicity Cards	£70
Misc. comic Non cartoon	£20

Cartoons

Davey Geo/Suffragette Series	£30
Valentine & Sons	£30
Nat Union of Women's Suffrage Soc.	£40
Artist's Suffrage League	£40
Other Publishers	£30

London Dock Strike of 1911   £30

STRIKES/MARCHES/UNREST

Seathwaite Navvy Riot 1904	£30
Leicester March to London 1905	£25
Belfast Strike 1907	£30
Laxey Miner's Strike 1907	£50
Winchester Riots 1908	£30
South Wales Coal Strike 1910	£30
Liverpool Strike 1910/11	
Carbonara Co.	£20
W. & Co.	£20
For full details on this series please refer to PPV 2003	
Cardiff Strike 1911	£30+
Llanelly Strike/Riots 1911	£30+
Thirlwell Strike 1911	£50
Ilkeston Strike 1912	
Coal Picking Scenes	£75
Sydney Street Siege 1911	£8
Smethwick 1913	£50
Tonypandy Riots 1913	£35
General Strike 1926	£25
London Dock Strike	£30
Worcester Railway Strike	£50
Demonstrations/Meetings	£20

121

RAILWAYS

As the dominant mode of transport in the Edwardian years, this subject was very well covered by the publishers of the time. The Railway Companies themselves led the way with a great number of sets and series extolling the virtue of travel on their own particular lines, and here the less common cards, or those from the smaller Companies, are highly sought after. As well as the correspondence cards listed here, many ordinary set cards were overprinted for correspondence or advertising use. These command a premium of no more than a couple of pounds.

Market report. Some of the scarcer official cards may be underpriced here as they are seen so infrequently. Prices need to be tested at auction along with the more unusual railway stations where catalogue prices are often left far behind.

OFFICIAL CARDS

A term used to describe postcards issued/sold by railway companies to gain revenue and to promote all aspects of their business. Subjects depicted include Hotels, Ships and Buses.

PRE-1923 COMPANIES

BARRY

Paddle Steamers	£10
Barry Island/Coloured view	£30
Barry Docks/Correspondence	£40

BELFAST AND COUNTY DOWN

Slieve Donard Hotel/Jotter	£10
Hotels/bw	£12

BIDEFORD, WESTWARD HO AND APPLEDORE

Views/Trains	£25

Caledonian rolling stock £5

CALEDONIAN

Engines/Rolling Stock

Sepia	£4
Coloured	£5

Hotels

General views	£5
Interiors/bw	£6
Interiors/Coloured	£8
Poster Adverts	£20

Views

Coloured/ Valentines	£4
coloured/ other	£6
Black/White	£10
Tartan Border	£8
Clyde Steamers/Clyde views	£10
Vignette/Multi-view/Pic both sides	£20
Green or Brown artwork/1903	£30

Poster Adverts

Shipping/Coloured	£30
Other types	£75

CALEDONIAN AND LNW

West Coast Joint Stock/Coloured	£8
Sleeping Car/Reservation card	£40

Royal Mail Route .

Coloured	£15
Black/White	£15

CALLANDER & OBAN

Ballachulish Hotel	£10
Views/Booklet sepia	£15

CAMBRIAN

Views	£6
Holiday Advertising/Correspondence	£12
Maps	£22
Vignette/PicturePostcard Co.	£25

CAMPBELTOWN & MACRIHANISH

Advertising	£80

CENTRAL LONDON

Celesque Series	£8
Maps/Rolling Stock	£20
1911 Strike	£50
Poster Adverts	£40

Exhibitions

Pillar Box Pullout	£35
Blow Card	£75

CHESHIRE LINES
Views/Correspondence	£30

CORK BANDON & SOUTH COAST
Views/Oilettes	£4

CORK BLACKROCK & PASSAGE
Paddle Steamer `Audrey'	£40

CORRIS
Views
Corris Railway Series/Photographic	£8
/Printed	£12
As above but Georges	£5

DISTRICT RAILWAY
Vignettes
Court size/Pictorial Postcard Syndicate	£40
Intermediate/Pictorial Postcard Company	£35

DUBLIN & SOUTH EASTERN
Hotel/Jotter	£10
Views/Correspondence	£30

DUBLIN, WICKLOW & WEXFORD
Peacock Series/Correspondence	£35
Views/Undivided Back	£35

DUMBARTON & BALLOCH JOINT LINES
Views
Black/White	£10
Coloured	£12

EAST COAST ROUTE
Flying Scotsman/Hildesheimer	£4
Views/Rolling Stock/Stations	£12
Vignette/Write Away	£10

FESTINIOG
Views/Photochrom	£8
Views/Valentines	£10
Poster Adverts	£90

FRESHWATER YARMOUTH & NEWPORT
Vignette/Picture Postcard Co.	£40

FURNESS
Engines & Rolling Stock/Series 18-19	£6
G. Romney Art/Series 12-13	£24
Exhibitions	£45
Poster Adverts/Series 21	£90

Views
Furness Abbey/Series 14-15	£1.50
McCorquodale	£4
Tuck/Series 1-7	£3
Tuck/Series 8	£4
Furness Abbey Hotel/Series 16-17	£6
HHH Series	£15
Sankey/Tours through Lakeland	£25
Vignettes/McCorquodale	£40

Steamers
Lake Steamers/Series 9-11	£5
Barrow & Fleetwood Steamers/Ser. 20	£15

GLASGOW & SOUTH WESTERN
Poster Adverts	£75

Steamers
McCorquodale	£3
Other publishers	£10

Hotels\
General views	£4
Multi-view	£6
Tuck/Chromo-litho	£10

Views
Oilettes	£5
Vignettes	£20

GREAT CENTRAL
Immingham Docks	£4
Hotels	£6
Engines/Rolling Stock	£18
Restaurant Car	£15
Poster Adverts	£65
Perforated Engine Card/	
Central Advertising Co.	£90

Shipping
Overprints on other company cards	£20
Printed	£14
Photographic	£16
Turner C.E.	£12
Steam Ship Department	£40
Tuck	£30

Views
Faulkner Series 545 & 546	£8
as / panel cards	£4
HHH Series	£20
Vignettes/Picture Postcard Co.	£30

GREAT EASTERN
Stations./Trains	£6
Hotels	£7
Underground Railway Maps of London	£6
Southwold Bus	£15
Poster Adverts	£100

Views
Crest on Picture/Oilettes	£3
Crest on Picture/bw	£4

Great Eastern £6

Shipping

Black & White	£8
Coloured	£10
Black & White/Correspondence	£12

Correspondence

General types	£25
Jarrold	£35
Oilette type	£25

Vignettes

Greetings from Harwich	£12
Tuck cathedrals	£75

Cathedrals

Faulkner/Series 118	£60
Faulkner with crest	£75

GREAT NORTH OF SCOTLAND

Views/Porter	£25
Cruden Bay Golf Tournament	£80
/Named Players	£100

Hotels

Palace Hotel Series	£15
Multi-view	£25
Multi-view/Pictures both sides	£30

Great Northern £30

GREAT NORTHERN

Hotels	£6
Correspondence	£25
Panoramic/Skegness & Sheringham	£30
Poster Adverts	£90

Engines

Photochrom	£2
Locomotive Publishing Co.	£5

Views

Photochrom/Coloured	£3
Black & White	£30

Vignettes

London views/Picture Postcard Co.	£25
Coloured	£40
Intermediate/Picture Postcard Co.	£35

GREAT NORTHERN & CITY

Views/bw Poster style	£35
Map	£50

GREAT NORTHERN/IRELAND

Correspondence	£15
Views/Overprint on picture	£25
Hotels/Multi-view	£18
Milroy Bay Motor Bus	£40

GREAT NORTHERN PICCADILLY &BROMPTON

Railway scenes	£10
Map	£25

GREAT SOUTHERN/IRELAND

Hotels	£6

GREAT SOUTHERN & WESTERN/ IRELAND

Views/Oilettes	£4
Joint with MGW/Wembley 1924	£25
Parknasilla Hotel/Motor Bus/	
Stage Coach Tours	£15
Poster Adverts/Parknasilla/	£70

Hotels

Jotter	£6
Lawrence/Correspondence	£12
Hotels in the Kingdom of Kerry	£20

GREAT WESTERN

Docks Series	£10
Fishguard Harbour/Route	£8
Motor Bus/Slough	£12
Restaurant Car/En Route	£18
Maps/with GWR crest	£40

Engines

Series 6	£2
Others	£4

Shipping

Photographic	£5
Coloured	£12

Views

Coloured or Sepia	£4

Hotels

General types	£4
Vignette	£8

Correspondence

General	£20
Wyndhams	£18

Poster Adverts

General types	£50
Series 3	£90

Vignettes

Intermediate/Picture Postcard Co.	£25
/London views	£30
Court Size/London views	£30

HAMPSTEAD TUBE
Views
Last Link	£6
Multi-view/Map on reverse	£12

HIGHLAND
Map/Correspondence	£75

Hotels
Inverness	£5
Others	£10

Views
Circular crest/bw	£12
Straight line inscription	£15
Highland Railway photos	£25
Early coloured/Red circular crest	£40

HULL & BARNSLEY
Scenes at Alexandra Dock etc.	£35
Views	£35
Train	£40

INVERGARRY & FORT AUGUSTUS
Views/Highland Railway series	£30

ISLE OF WIGHT
Vignettes/Picture Postcard Co.	£35

ISLE OF WIGHT CENTRAL
Vignettes/Picture Postcard Co.	£35
Views	£40

JOINT SOUTH WESTERN & BRIGHTON
Vignettes/Picture Postcard Co.	£35

KENT & EAST SUSSEX
Engines/Correspondence	£8
Views/1-6	£7
Other Correspondence cards	£35

LANCASHIRE & YORKSHIRE
Correspondence	£30
Vignettes/Picture Postcard Co.	£25

Engines/Rolling Stock
General issues	£3
Overprinted French	£6

Views
1905 &1907 series	£3
New series	£4
Overprinted French/All series	£5

Shipping
1907 series	£4
New series	£6
Overprinted French/All series	£7
Liverpool and Drogheda Steamers	£35

LIVERPOOL OVERHEAD
Dock views	£25

LONDON, BRIGHTON & SOUTH COAST
Correspondence	£40

Poster Adverts	£90

Views
Waterlow/Series 1-6	£4

Vignettes
French vignettes/Red overprint	£15
Picture Postcard Co.	£25

LONDON, CHATHAM & DOVER
Vignettes/Court Size
Black/White	£25
Coloured	£35

London & North Western Kitchen £4

LONDON & NORTH WESTERN
McCorquodale
Engines/Rolling Stock	£1.50/£4
Views	£1.50
Hotels	£4
Shipping	£3
Buses/Lorries etc.	£10
/Horse drawn	£6
Exhibitions	£20
Poster Adverts	£100
Maps/Correspondence	£100

Tuck
Coloured/Royal Trains etc.	£1
Engines/Rolling Stock	£2
Views	£3
Shipping	£4
Hotels	£4

St. Louis Exposition/Undivided back
Exhibits/Multi-view	£6
Tuck/bw	£10
Tuck/Coloured	£15

LONDON & SOUTH WESTERN
Orphanage	£4
View with crest/Correspondence	£40

Shipping
Black/White	£6
Coloured/Early	£18

Poster Adverts

Southampton Hotel	£45
Other Posters	£80

Vignettes

Pictorial Postcard Syndicate	£35
Intermediate/Picture Postcard Co.	£22
London views/Picture Postcard Co.	£22

London Underground £35

LONDON UNDERGROUND ELECTRIC
Poster Adverts

W.H.S.	£40
London Nooks and Corners	£40
Other types	£35

LONDONDERRY & LOUGH SWILLY

Map/Correspondence	£60

LYNTON & BARNSTAPLE

Views/Stations/Trains	£18

MARYPORT & CARLISLE

Map/Correspondence	£90

MERSEY

Views/Stations/Lifts/Trains	£12
Poster Advert	£80

METROPOLITAN

Correspondence	£12
Maps	£12

VIEWS

Sepia/1-30	£5
Black/White	£15

METROPOLITAN DISTRICT

Engines/Rolling Stock	£5

Midland Railway £75

MIDLAND

Engines	£2
Rolling Stock	£8
Midland Express/St. Pancras	£5
Ships	£6
Carriages	£10
Exhibitions	£18
Maps	£18
Heysham Electric Train	£25

Views

Photochrom	£4
Nearest Station/Coloured	£12

Hotels

General types	£4
Vignettes/Coloured	£6
/Travel & Entertainment	£30
/BW & Sepia	£18
Midland Grand Hotel/Business Lunch	£90

Vignettes

Black/White	£15
Coloured/Andrew Reid	£20

Poster Adverts

General types	£25
Series	£75

MIDLAND & GREAT NORTHERN JOINT
Views/Correspondence   £40

MIDLAND GREAT WESTERN
Hotels   £6
Wembley Exhibition/Trade Stand   £15

MIDLAND/NORTHERN COUNTIES COMMITTEE
Trains   £12
Views/Correspondence   £35

NEWPORT GODSHILL & ST.LAWRENCE
Vignette/Picture Postcard Co.   £35

NORTH BRITISH
Ships/Coloured   £6
Ships/BW with crest   £12
Scottish Exhibition/Poster overprint   £40

Hotels
General types   £3
Poster Adverts   £8

Views
NBR Series/Caledonia 129   £3
Black/White & Coloured   £12
With crest   £14
Photo/White or decorated border   £15

NORTH EASTERN
Hotels/ York & Newcastle   £2
Hotels/ Others   £5
Riverside Quay/Hull   £5
Newcastle Electric Trains   £6
Brussels Exhibition   £12
Steam Goods Lorry   £50

Views
Photo Panoramic/1-40   £25
/Maps below picture   £30

Poster Adverts
General types   £75
Industrial Poster Reproductions   £90

NORTH STAFFORDSHIRE
Correspondence   £15

Views
McCorquodale/W&K   £4
W&K and W&TG/White border   £7
Golf   £30
Glossy anon.   £15

PORTPATRICK & WIGTOWNSHIRE JOINT
Ships   £18
Views   £35

SNOWDON MOUNTAIN RAILWAY
General types   £4
Snowdon Series/1-90   £8

Maps   £40
Poster Adverts   £60

Court Cards
Advertising/Hotel & Railway   £65

SOMERSET & DORSET JOINT
Views/Correspondence   £60

South Eastern & Chatham £3

SOUTH EASTERN AND CHATHAM
Views/McCorquodale   £3
Engines/Rolling Stock   £3
Stations/Trains   £4
Hotels   £6
Ships   £4
London-Paris/English or French   £12
Bologne views/Stevenard   £12
Exhibitions   £8
Views/Correspondence   £25
Maps   £22
Poster Adverts   £90

SOUTH EASTERN & CHATHAM & DOVER
Vignettes
London views/Picture Postcard Co. etc. £20
Intermediate/Picture Postcard Co.   £25
Pictorial Postcard Syndicate   £35

STRATFORD-ON-AVON & MIDLAND JUNCTION
Poster Advert   £100

VALE OF RHEIDOL
Views/Advertising overprints   £15

WEST CLARE
Views   £25

WEST HIGHLAND
Views   £6

WESTON, CLEVEDON & PORTISHEAD LIGHT
Train   £35

WICK AND LYBSTER
Views/Highland Railway Series   £35

WIRRAL
Views/Correspondence	£60
Map/Correspondence	£80

POST - 1923 COMPANIES
GREAT WESTERN
Engines	£3
Views	£4
Hotels	£4
KGV/Folded locomotive card	£75
Poster Adverts	£60

LONDON MIDLAND & SCOTTISH
Engines	£3
Hotels	£4
Ships	£6
Camping Coaches	£12
Views/Holiday tickets	£12
Container services/Removals	£35
Poster Adverts	£30

LONDON & NORTH EASTERN
Engines/Trains	£4
Hotels	£4
Ships	£8
Views	£8
Camping Coaches	£10
Paddle Steamers	£6
Poster Adverts	£90
Northern Belle Cruise Train	
Unused	£25
Used on Train with Cachet	£75

Southern Railway £3

SOUTHERN
Engines/Trains	£3
Ships	£5
Poster Adverts/LBSCR	£90
Views	
Coloured/L. Richmond	£25
Correspondence	£35

POST-1947/BRITISH RAILWAYS
Hotels	£3
Ships	£3
Trains	£3
Gleneagles/Turnberry Golf Courses	£10
Seaspeed/Hovercraft	£1.50
Birmingham/New St. Station	£4
Correspondence	£4
Kyle of Lochalsh Station	£5
Poster Adverts	£15

NON-OFFICIAL CARDS
ACCIDENTS
Cudworth	£6
Grantham 1906	£4
Shrewsbury 1907	£6
Salisbury 1906	£6
Witham1905	£4
W. Gothard/In Memoriam type	£15/£75
Miscellaneous	£15+

The Overland Ltd , Chicago £3

OVERSEAS RAILWAYS
Engines	£3
Rolling Stock	£3
Stations	£1.50+
Views	£3
Official Cards/Crest or Title	£4
Japanese Official	£5

FRENCH POSTERS/OFFICIAL ISSUES
Orleans post-1920	£8
Artist signed	£12
Chemins de Fer de l'Quest	£8
Chromo-litho/Undivided back	£25

FUNICULAR & CLIFF RAILWAYS/LIFTS
Lynton-Lynmouth	£2
Other UK	£5
Overseas	£3

LOCOMOTIVES

Oilettes	£3
OJ Morris	£3
E.Pouteau	£4
Locomotive PublishingCo. / F.Moore	£2.50
Real Photographic	£2
France/F. Fleury	£3
Other Artist Drawn cards	£2.50

MINIATURE RAILWAYS

Eskdale Express R/P £5

Ravenglass & Eskdale	£5
Romney, Hythe & Dymchurch	£3
Volk's Electric Railway	£3
Other Railways	£6

MISCELLANEOUS

Animated Scenes	£10
Bridges/Tunnels/Viaducts	£4
Level Crossings	£20
Locomotive Works	£12
Locomotive Sheds	£6
Motor buses/ road vehicles	£20
Railway Staff	£8
Signal Boxes	£15
Trains on the Line	£3
Hospital trains	£3

Locomotive Publishing Co.

Vignettes/Coloured	£30
Vignettes/Monochrome	£25

MOUNTAIN RAILWAYS

Snowdon/Non-Official	£1.50
Overseas	£2

NARROW GAUGE

Vale of Rheidol	£3
Others	£6

RAILWAY STATIONS
Large City Stations

Interior	£8
Exterior	£4

Others

Interior	£40
Exterior	£20

Havant Railway Station super R/P £40

Lancing Station R/P £30

UNDERGROUND RAILWAYS

London Transport	£10
Foreign/U. Bahnes/Metros	£6

Underground Lift operators R/P £30

ROAD TRANSPORT

The majority of these cards were the work of the town or village photographer and produced for the local topographical market. Consequently they were never issued in any great number, which is why they are so highly rated today. There is an insatiable demand for unusual photographic studies, particularly where there is an added topographical element.

BUSES

Steam	£40
Horse-drawn	
Real Photographic (close up)	£30/£50
Printed	£15
London horse-drawn/Coloured	£10
Motor	
Real Photographic	£40
Printed	£20

It is pointed out that for all relevant entries e.g. Buses, Lorries, Traction Engines, Trams etc. the stated prices are for cards, either RP or Printed, fully identified and showing a 'Close-up at a named location' with real photographic cards being the most desirable. Unlocated cards and middle or far-distance views would be priced accordingly.

Trolleybuses

Pre-1939	£25
1940 onwards	£12

Derby Bus station R/P £20

Motor Bus Superb R/P £40

Coaches/Single-deck   £12/£20
There are in circulation many privately produced, postcard-size, plain back photographs of Buses and Trams.
Most of these have been printed in quantity from an existing negative and consequently have only a nominal value.

Real Photo R/P £8

Coach R/P £ 12

Charabancs

Whole Vehicle	£8
Part Vehicle	£3

LORRIES

Petrol Tankers	£30
Vans	£25
Coachbuilders' advertising cards/	
RP studies of Lorries/Removal Vans	£6

Steam

Commercial	£40
Military	£25

Motor

Lorry Fleets/Groups/RP	£50
Commercial	£30
Military	£25

Advert Cards

Poster Type	£35
Other Adverts	£12

Where applicable, prices are for trade vehicles sign-written with company name and location.

Lorry R/P £30

Morris Advert £12

MOTOR CYCLES

Close-up	£20
With Sidecar	£20

Advert Cards

Poster Type (Colour)	£35
Other Adverts	£12

MOTOR RACING
MOTOR CYCLE RACING
SEE SPORT PAGES 158-163

TRACTION ENGINES

Showmans	£50
Commercial	£30
Agricultural	£30
Military	£20
Steam Rollers	£30
Repair Gangs	£25
Accidents	£50

There are in circulation many privately produced, postcard-size, plain back photographs of Fairground and Showman's engines.
Most of these have been printed in quantity from an existing negative and consequently have a nominal value of maybe £5

Real Photo, with sidecar £20

Royal Mail Motor Cycle R/P £35

MOTOR CARS

Pre-1918	£12
1918-1939	£8
1940 onwards	£5
Garages	£30
Exhibitions/GB and Foreign	£6
Factories and Works/Interiors	£12
Celebrities of the Motoring World/	
Set 6/Tuck Oilette 9017	£6

Advert cards

Poster Type	£35
Other Adverts/Pre-1939	£15
/1940 onwards	£5

OTHER TRANSPORT

Ambulances

Horse-drawn	£35
Motor	£20

Fire Engines

Hand Drawn	£40
Horse Drawn	£40
Motor	£40

Royal Mail Vans	£35

TRAMS

Steam Trams	£35
Electric Trams	£35
Horse-drawn Trams	£35
Track-laying/Removal	£35
Trials	£30
Opening Ceremonies	£35
First Tram	£35
Last Tram	£20
Commemorative Cards	£25
In Memoriam Cards	£15
Tram Graveyards Early	£35
Decorated Cars	£6
Depots	£35
Works Vehicles	£30
Douglas S.E. Tramway	£6

Wallington Tram R/P £35

AA Patrolman helping a car through the flood. R/P £22

Traffic congestion due to tramline priority £10

Close Up Tram R/P £35

ROYALTY

I think the British Royal Family, and the many European dynasties at the turn of the century, must have been looked upon as a commercial goldmine by the Edwardian publishers. The vast numbers of cards handed down to us bears adequate testimony to their popularity at the time, when all types of Royal personages and Events both British and Foreign were subject to volume output by the picture postcard industry. I suppose the same is true today, as interest in this field has continued unabated through the years. And yet, it is perhaps fair to say that the wide public interest in Royalty and their doings, is not reflected in current price levels for historical picture postcards, for while the more unusual Portraits and Events will always sell, as will the many superb chromo-litho foreign commemorative issues, the bulk of the catalogue consisting of the more common GB types has always proved difficult.

Market Report
The monarchy is proving to be surprisingly resilient. Royal visits and Asian royalty (except Japan) are treated with due deference. While there is a huge over-supply of common material about, stock is still moving if priced accordingly.

GREAT BRITAIN
QUEEN VICTORIA
Diamond Jubilee 1897

p.u. 1897	£125
Unused	£65

Mourning Cards 1901	£15

Portraits	£8

KING EDWARD VII
Royal Tour 1901/'Ophir'
Wrench/Links of Empire/Set 20

p.u. from Ports of Call	£30
Unposted	£15

Royal Tour 1901 / 'Ophir'
Tuck R. & Sons/Empire Series 1649

p.u. from Ports of Call	£30
Unposted	£15

Coronation 1902
Tuck R. & Sons/Coronation Series/

Embossed	£10
Stewart & Woolf/Set 10	£10
H.Cassiers/London View Series	£8
Other Souvenir Cards	£6
Coronation Souvenir/bw	£4
Coronation Procession	£2

Visits to Paris 1903

Tuck R. & Sons/Set 10	£6
Voisey Chas./Set 15	£8

Death 1910

Mourning Cards	£2
Funeral Procession	£1

Visits

GB	£12
Foreign	£8
Portraits	£1.50

KING GEORGE V
Coronation 1911

Souvenir Cards	£3
Coronation Procession	£1

Delhi Durbar 1911	£3

Silver Jubilee 1935

Souvenir Cards	£3
Procession	£1

Death 1936

Mourning Cards	£3
Funeral Procession	£1.50

Visits

GB	£12
Foreign	£6
Portraits	£1

King Edward VII Oillette Card £6

Raphael Tuck 'Kings and Queens of England' £12

KING EDWARD VIII
Investiture as Prince of Wales 1911	£3
Coronation Souvenir	£6
Wedding Souvenir	£35
With Mrs Simpson	£40
Visits	
GB	£20
Foreign	£15
Portraits	£2

KING GEORGE VI
Coronation 1937
Souvenir Cards	£4
Coronation Procession	£2
Visit to France 1938	£10
Victory Celebrations 1945	£5
Mourning Cards 1952	£10
Visits	
GB	£12
Foreign	£8
Portraits	£1.50

QUEEN ELIZABETH II
Marriage 1947
Souvenir Cards	£5
Betrothal Souvenir Cards	£3
Coronation 1953	
Souvenir Cards	£2

Coronation Procession	£1
Prince of Wales Investiture 1969	£1.50
Silver Wedding 1972	£1
Silver Jubilee 1977	£1
Visits/Pre-1970	
GB	£6
Foreign	£4
Portraits	£1/£4

MISCELLANEOUS EVENTS
Coronation Bonfires	£20
Proclamations	£10
Royal Gatherings	£2
Royal Weddings	£3

N.B. Portraits include family groups. Less photographed members of the Royal Family, e.g. Prince John, together with other examples of minor Royalty, would be worth around £1.50+.

SERIES
Kings & Queens of England
Tuck R. & Sons/Set 42
Price per card	£12
King Insurance Co.	£6
Faulkners Series	£8

Early Swedish Royalty portrait £8

OVERSEAS

It will be seen that an equivalent list to the foregoing could be produced for every country in the world which has had a Monarchy at any time since 1869! This remains a vast, uncharted field, where much research is yet to be done. I give below a general guide to price for the Commemorative Souvenir cards already known.

ROYAL EVENTS

1888-1891	£50
1892-1895	£35
1896-1899	£25
1900-1902	£20
1903-1907	£15
1908-1914	£10
1915 onwards	£5

Russian royalty, French published card £20

PORTRAITS

Balkans/Eastern Europe	£8-£12
Belgium/Spain	£3
Other Countries	£6-£10
Weddings	£6

Russia

Russian published cards	£25-£30
Continental Publishers	£20-£30
Cartoons	£25
British Publishers	£20-£25

Early Royal events 1910 £10

Russian Royalty, £25

The Art of Shipping
Hans Bohrdt 1857-1945

Above; Hamburg America Line   *Meissner & Buch series 1012*

Above; Muhlmeister & Johler - "Auguste Victoria"

Hans Bohrdt was a marine artist at the German Court and a friend of Kaiser Wilhelm II. All the cards on this page were produced for the Hamburg-Amerika Line for whom he did most of his steamship paintings.

Right; "SS Herth" in Hong Kong

Right; "Lensahn"

Wishing you many happy returns of the day.

SHIPPING

A great number of cards were issued during the early years of the century, and indeed later, perhaps reflecting the dependence which an island nation placed upon the sea. Always a popular theme with collectors, there has been a steady supply of new cards issued on this subject, thanks largely to the many Shipping Companies, who continued publishing through out the depressed inter-war years, when the flow of more general cards abated.

Market Report; There is an insatiable demand for any quality material. Prices for the best cards will continue to rise. At the same time there are heavily remaindered stocks of cards on the market - particularly Cunard material which needs to be avoided.

AMERICAN LINE
Hamburg - New York

This is list of all the shipping Companies known to have published postcards of their ships and routes. This list is not complete, and probably never can be, and will be added to as more information becomes available. To list each Company along with the types of postcards produced by each has therefore become impractical. It would become a catalogue in itself - remembering that there were thousands of shipping companies, that some had hundreds of vessels and that some ships had many postcard images published (of varying scarcity). The result is that it is only practicable to suggest general guide lines as to values in this catalogue. Some ships, like the "Titanic" and "Olympic", will always have more interest.

The popular artist-impression postcards are best viewed in Christopher Deakes's "A Postcard History of the Passenger Liner" which has short biographies of many artists. Values of postcard by specific artists are included in the main Artists Section of this Catalogue. Shipbuilding companies from around the world have also published postcards of ships that they have built and, in general these are not so easy to find. The suggested values are as follows:

American Line £20

Chromolithographic advertising	**£25-£75**
Poster advertising	**£20-£60**
Japanese inset types	**£12**
Artist Impressions	**£4-£20**
Real photographs (officials)	**£6-£10**
Real photographs	**£4-£15**
Printed photographs (officials)	**£2-£10**
Printed photographs	**£1-£8**
Interiors (artist impressions)	**£5-£20**
Interiors (photographic)	**£3-£8**
Japanese ship-launch cards (post war) £4	

We have introduced a star system - No star, One star and two stars - with 2 stars being the higher value. The cards are presumed to be Pre-1939 and in good condition.

Readers should be aware that the rating will depend on the popularity, not necessarily the scarcity, of a company - many people will not have even know that some companies produced cards therefore they do not necessarily have a scarcity value - but good art cards, for example, could influence this. Obviously many cards will be much more common but within these companies there are likely to be ships worth more.

R.M.S. "TUNISIAN."

Allan Line £25

ABC Steamship Line (GB)*
Aberdeen & Commonwealth Line (GB)
Aberdeen Direct Line (Rennie) (GB)*8
Aberdeen Line (GB)*
Aberdeen Steam Navigation Co (GB)
Aberdeen, Newcastle & Hull (GB)*
Adelaide Steamship (Australia)*
Adler Linie (Germany)
Admiral Line (USA)
Adria Co (Austria/Italy)*
African Steamship Co (GB)
Afrikanische Frucht-Comapgnie (Germany)
Alaska Cruises Inc (USA)
Alaska Steam Ship Co (USA)
Albion Steamship Co (GB)*
Alcoa Steamship Co (USA)
Alexandria Navigation Co (Egypt)
Allan Line (Canada)*
American Banner Line (USA)
American Export Lines (USA)
American Hawaii Cruises (USA)
American Hawaiian Line (USA)
American Line (USA)*
American Mail Lines (USA)
American Merchant Lines (USA)
American Pioneer Line (USA)
American President Lines (USA)
American South African Line (USA)
Amsterdam, Reederij, (Holland)

Anchor Line £12

Anchor Line (GB)
Anchor-Donaldson Line (GB)
Anek Lines (Greece)
Anglo-American Nile & Tourist Co (GB)*
Anglo-Egyptian Mail Line (GB)*
A-O Lines (GB)
Apcar Line (GB)**
Argo Reederei (Germany)*
Arosa Line (Panama)
Athel Line (GB)
Atlantic Steam Navigation Co (GB)
Atlantic Transport Lines (USA)*

Atlantic Transport £6

Atlanttrafik, AB, (Sweden)
Austasia Line (GB)
Australasian United Steam Navigation (AUSN) (GB)*
Australian Commonwealth Line (Australia)
Australian-Oriental Line (GB)

Australia-West Pacific Line (Norway)
Australind Steam Navigation Co (GB)
Austrian Lloyd (Austria)**
Avenue Shipping (GB)
Aznar Line (Spain)
Bailey & Leetham (GB)**
Baltic American Line (Denmark)**
Baltic State Shipping Line (USSR)
Baltimore & Carolina Steamship Co (USA)
Baltimore Insular Lines (USA)
Baltimore Mail Line (USA)
Baltimore Steam Packet (USA)_
Bank Line (GB)
Barber Lines (Norway)
Barry & Bristol Channel (GB)*
Batavier Line (Holland)
Bateaux ?Moulettes? (France)
Belfast Steamship Co (GB)
Belgian Fruit Lines (Belgium)
Belle Steamers (GB)

Belle Steamers £8

Ben Line (GB)
Bennett Line (GB)**
Bergen Line (B&N Line) (Norway)
Bermuda Star Line (USA)
Bibby Line (GB)*
Birkenhead Corporation Ferries (GB)
Black Ball Line (Canada)
Black Sea Steamship Line (USSR)

Bibby Line £8

Black Star Line (Ghana)
Bland Line (Gibraltar)*
Blue Funnel Line (GB)**
Blue Star Line (GB)*
Bombay Steam Navigation Co (India)**
Booker Line (GB)
Booth Line (GB)*
Bore Line (Finland)
Bornholm Line (Denmark)
Botel Cruises (Holland)
Bournemouth & South Coast SP Co (GB)
Bowater Steam Ship Co (GB)
Bristol Steam Navigation Co (GB)
British & African Steamship Co (GB)
British Columbia Ferries (Canada)
British India Steam Navigation Co (GB)*
British Petroleum (BP) (GB)
British Tanker Co (GD)
Brodin Line (Sweden)
Broere NV, Gebr.,   (Holland)
Brostrom Shipping (Sweden)
Brugge-Sluis (Du)
Bruns, W., & Co (Germany)
Bucknall Steamship Lines (GB)*
Bull Lines (USA)
Buries Markes Ltd (GB)
Burns Line (GB)
Burns, Philp & Co (Australia)*
Cairn Line (GB)*

Caledonian Steam Packet Co (GB)

Caltex (World)

Campbell, P&A., (GB)

Canada Steamship Lines (Canada)

Canadian Australasian Line (Can/NZ)

Canadian National Steamships (Canada)

Canadian Northern Steamship (Canada)

Canadian Pacific Steamships (Canada/GB)*

Canadian Pacific Steamships £7

Canguro Linee (Italy)

Cape Cod SS Co (USA)

Caribbean Cruise Lines (USA)

Carnival Cruise Lines (USA)

Carron Line (GB)*

Cassar Co (Malta)**

Castle Line (GB)**

Cawston (GB)

Central Hudson Steamboat (USA)

Chandris Lines (Greece)

Chemin de Fer du Congo Superior (Belgium)**

Chia. Nacional de Navegacao (Portugal)

Chia. Nacional de Navegacao Costeira (Brazil)**

Chicago Duluth Transit Co (USA)

China Mail Steamship Co (USA)

China Navigation Co (GB)*

Cia. Anonima Venezolana de Navegacion (Venezuela)

China Navigation Co. £40

Cia. Argentina de Navegacion Dodero (Argentina)

Cia. Maritima Frutera (Spain)

Cia. Transoceanica Argentina (Argentina)*

Cia. Trasatlantica (Spain)*

Cia. Trasmediterranea (Spain)*

Cie. Auxiliaire de Navigation (France)

Cie. de Affreteurs Reunis (France)

Cie. de Navigation Charles le Borgne (France)

Cie. de Navigation Fraissinet & Cyprien Fabre (France)

Cie. de Navigation Mixte (France)

Cie. de Navigation Paquet (France)

Cie. de Navigation Sud-Atlantique (France)

Cie. de Transports Maritimes de l?AOF (France)

Cie. des Chargeurs Reunis (France)

Cie. des Messageries Maritimes (France)*

Cie. Fraissinet (France)

Cie. Generale Transatlantique (France)

Cie. Havraise de Navigation (France)

Cie. Havraise Peninsulaire (France)

Cie. Maritime Belge du Congo (Belgium)*

Cie. Nationale de Navigation (France)

Cie. Nationale de Navigation de Grece (Greece)

Cities Service Tankers (USA)

CITRA (Italy)*

City Line (GB)*
City of Cork Steam Packet Co (GB)
City of Dublin Steam Packet Co (GB)*
City Steamboat Co (GB)
Clan Line (GB)
Clarke Steamship Co (Canada)*
Clarkson's Cruises (GB)
Cleveland & Buffalo Line (USA)
Clipper Line (Sweden)
Clyde Line (USA)*
Clyde Shipping Co (GB)*
Clyde-Mallory Line (USA)
Coast Lines (GB)

M.V. "IRISH COAST" (3824 Tons)

Coast Lines £5

Cogedar Line (Italy)
Colombian Line (USA)*
Colonial Navigation Co (USA)
Colwyn Bay & Liverpool SS Co (GB)**
Common Brothers (GB)
Commonwealth & Dominion Line (GB)
Concordia Line (Norway)
Constantine Line (GB)
Cook's Tourist Steamers (GB)
Corsica Ferries (Italy)
Cory, William, & Son (GB)
Cosens & Co (GB)
Costa Line (Italy)
Crescent Shipping Lines (Pakistan)

Cunard Line (GB)
Cunard White Star (GB)
Currie Line (GB)
Cusolich Line (Austria/Italy)*
Dairen Kisen Kaisha (Japan)*
Dalen, Rederi, (Sweden)
Dansk-Statsbaner (DSB) (Denmark)
De la Rama Lines (USA)
Deilmann, Peter, (Germany)
Delta Line (USA)
Denholm, J&J, Ltd (GB)
Detroit & Cleveland Line (USA)
Deutsche Eisenbahn (Germany)
Deutsche Levante Linie (Germany)
Deutsche Ost-Afrika Linie (Germany)**
Deutsche Seereederie (East Germany)
DFDS (Denmark)
Di Giorgio SS Line (USA)*
Direct Line (GB)*
Doeksen, Reederij,
Dollar Steamship Lines (USA)
Dominion Far East Line (GB)
Dominion Line (GB)

Dominion Line £8

Donaldson Line (GB)
Drake Shipping Co (GB)
Dublin & Manchester Line (GB)*
Dublin & Silloth Line (GB)*

Dubrovacka Parobrodska Plovidba
(Yugoslavia)

Dundee & Newcastle Steam Shipping (GB)*

Dundee, Perth & London Shipping Co (GB)**

East African Railways (GB)*

Eastern & Australian Line (GB)*

Eastern Mediterranean Express Line (GB)*

Eastern Shipping Corporation (India)

Egyptian Mail Steamship Lines (GB)**

Egyptian Shipping Co (GB)

Elder Dempster Lines (GB)

Elder Dempster Lines £10
Elders & Fyffes(GB)*

Ellerman & Bucknall Steamships (GB)

Ellerman & Papayanni Lines (GB)*

Ellerman Lines (GB)

Ellerman's City Line (GB)

Ellerman's Hall Line (GB)

Ellerman's Wilson Line (GB)

ELMA (Argentina)

Empresa Insulana de Navegacao (Portugal)

Enkhuizen-Stavoren (Holland)

Enterprise Transportation Co (USA)

Epirotiki Line (Greece)

Epirus Line (Greece)

Erste Donau (Austria)

Ertslijn (Holland)

Esso Petroeum (international)

Europe Canada Line (Panama)

Europe-Australia Line (Greece)

Euxine Shipping (GB)

Everard, F.T.., & Sons. (GB)

Fabre Line (France)

Fall River Line (USA)

FANU (Argentina)*

Far-Eastern Steamship Co (USSR)

Farrell Lines (USA)

Fearnley & Eger (Norway)

Federal Steam Navigation (GB)

Ferrovie dello Stato (Italy)*

FHS (Federal-Houlder-Shire) (GB)*

Finland Steamship Co (Finland)*

Finska Angfartygs Aktiebolaget (Finland)*

Fisher, Renwick & Co (GB)

Flota Argentina de Navegacion de Ultramar (FANU) (Argentina)*

Flota Mercante del Estado (Argentina)*

Flotta Lauro (Italy)

Flushing Line (Holland)

Fragline (Greece)

France, Fenwick & Co (GB)*

Fratelli Grimaldi Armatori (Italy)

Fraternitas, Rederi, (Sweden)

French Line (CGT) (France)

Fritzen & Sohn, Johs., (Germany)

Furness Bermuda Line (GB)

Furness Lines (GB)*

Fyffes (GB)*

Furness Line £12

Gdynia-America Line (Poland)

General Steam Navigation Co (GB)

Glen Line (GB)"

Goodrich Transit Co (USA)

Gorthon Lines (Sweden)

Gota Kanal Rederi (Sweden)

Goteborg-Frederikshavn Linjen (Sweden)

Gothabolaget (Sweden)

Gotland, Angfartygs Ab, (Sweden)

Grace Line (USA)

Hamburg Amerika Line £15

Grace Line £5

Grand Trunk Pacific Steamship (Canada)

Grangesbergsbolaget (Sweden)

Great Lakes Transit Corporation USA)

Great Northern Pacific SS Co (USA)

Greek Australian Line (Greece)

Greek Line (Greece)

Grimaldi-Siosa Line (Italy)

Gulf Line (GB)**

Haaland (Norway)

Hadag (Germany)

Hafen Dampschiff. AG (Germany)

Haj Line (India)**

Hall?s Line (GB)

Hamburg & Anglo-American Nile Co

Hamburg-Amerika Linie (Germany)**

Hamburg-Atlantic Linie (Germany)

Hamburg-Bremer-Afrika Linien (Germany)

Hamburg-Sudamerika Linie (Germany)*

Hansa, Deutsche Dampfschiff, Gesell. (Germany)

HAPAG (Germany)

Hapag-Lloyd (Germany)

Harrison, T&J., Line (GB)

Havenlijn (Holland)

Hawaiian Steamship Co (USA)

Hellenic Mediterranean Lines (Greece)

Helsingborg, Rederi Aktiebolaget, (Sweden)

Henderson Line (GB)*

Holland Afrika Line (Holland)

Holland Friesland Lijn (Holland)

Holland Ireland Line (Holland)

Holland Steamship Co (Holland)

Holland Veluwe Lijn (Holland)

Holland West-Afrika Lijn (Holland)

Holland-Amerika Lijn (Holland)

Holt, John, Line (GB)

Home Lines (Panama)

Hong Kong, Canton & Macau Steamboat (GB)**

Horn Linie (Germany)

Hough Line (GB)*

Houlder Line (GB)

Howard Smith Ltd (Australia)*

Huddard, Parker (Australia)

Hudson Navigation Co (USA)

Hudson River Day Line (USA)

Iberian Star Line (Panama)

Imperial Department Railways (Japan)
Imperial Direct West India Mail (GB)**
Incres Line (USA)*
Independent Gulf Line (Holland)
Indiana Transport (USA)
Indiana Transportation Co (USA)
Indo-China Steam Navigation Co (GB)*
Instone Line (GB)*
Inter-Island Steam Navigation Co (USA)
Intourist (USSR)
Irish Shipping Ltd (Ireland)
Irrawaddy Flotilla Co (GB)**
Isbrandtsen Lines (USA)
Island Tug & Barge (Canada)
Islands Steamship (Iceland)*
Isle of Man Steam Packet Co (GB)
Isles of Scilly SS Co (GB)

Italia Line (Soc. Per Azioni di Navigazione) (Italy)
Ivaran Lines (Norway)
Jadranska Plovidba (Yugoslavia)
Jakob Lines (Finland)
Jamaica Banana Producers SS Co (GB)*

Jamaica Banana Producers Co. £12

Japan Line (Japan)
Japanese Railways (Japan)
Jardine Mathison (GB)*
Johnson Line (Sweden)

Johnston Warren Lines (GB)
Jugoslavenski Lloyd (Yugoslavia)
Karageorgis Lines (Greece)
Kavounides Line (Greece)
KdF (Germany)*
Khedivial Mail Line (GB)**
Kingsin Linie (Germany)**
Kinkai Yusen   KK (Japan)
Knutsen Line (Norway)
Kokusai Kisen Kaisha (Japan)*
Koln-Dusseldorfer (Germany)
Koln-Dusseldorfer Rheindamfschiffahrt (Germany)
Kolokotronis Lines (Greece)
Koninklijke Hollandsche Lloyd (Holland)

Koninklijke Java-China Pakepvaart Lijnen (Holland)

Koninklijke Nederlandsche Stoomboot Maats (KNSM) (Holland)

Koninklijke Paketvaart Maats (KPM) (Holland)*

Koninklijke Paketvaart Maats £10

Koninklijke Rotterdamsche Lloyd (Holland)
Kosmos Linie (Germany)**
Kreisschiffahrt (Germany)
Kriton Shipping (Greece)
La Veloce (Italy)*
Laegterkompaniet (Norway)
Laeisz, F., (Germany)

Lamey Tugs (GB)

Lamport & Holt Line (GB)*

Langlands & Sons (GB)

Lassman (Russia)**

Lauritzen, J., (Denmark)

Lauro Lines (Italy)

Leonhardt & Blimberg (Germany)

Leyland Line (GB)**

Libra Maritime (Greece)

Lindblad Travel (USA)

Linea 'C' (Italy)

Lineas Maritimas Argentinas (ELMA)
(Argentina)*

Liverpool& North Wales Steamship Co (GB)*

Lloyd Austriaco (Austria)**

Lloyd Brazileiro (Brazil)**

Lloyd Genovese (Italy)*

Lloyd Italiano (Italy)

Lloyd Royal Belge (Belgium)*

Lloyd Sabaudo (Italy)*

Lloyd Triestino (Italy)

Lloyd Triestino £8

London & Edinburgh Shipping Co (GB)

London & Overseas Freighters (GB)

London County Council (GB)

London Missionary Society (GB)

Los Angeles Steamship Co (USA)

Lubeck Linie (Germany)

Lund?s Blue Anchor Line (GB)**

Lykes Bros. Steamship Co (USA)

Lyle Shipping Co (GB)

MacAndrews & Co (GB)

MacBrayne, David, Ltd (GB)*

MacIver Line (GB)

Maersk Line (Denmark)

Manchester Liners (GB)

Metcalf Motor Coasters (GB)

Marittima Italiana (Italy)

Matson Navigation Co (USA)*

McIlwraith, McEearcharn Line (Australia)

Mediterranean Sun Line Lines (Greece)

Melbourne Steamship Line (Australia)

Merchants & Miners Transportation Co
(USA)*

Mersey Docks & Harbour Board (GB)

Messina, Ignacio, &Co (Italy)

Meyer Line (Norway)

Miami Steamship Co (USA)

Military Sea Transportation Service (USA)

Mitsui Line (Japan)*

Mitsui OSK Lines (Japan)

Mobil (international)

Mogul Line (India)*

Monticello SS Co (USA)

Moore-McCormack Lines (USA)

Morgan Line (USA)

Moore-McCormack Lines £8

Morocco, Canary Islands & Madeira Line (GB)*

Mory & Cie (France)

Moss Hutchinson (GB)

Moss Steamship (GB)*

Muller, Wm.H., & Co (Holland)

Munson Steamship Co (USA)

Murmansk Shipping Co (USSR)

Muskoka Navigation Co (Canada)

Naias Shipping (Greece)

Natal Line (GB)*

National Hellenic American Line (Greece)

Nautilus Steam Shipping Co (GB)

Naviera Aznar (Spain)

Naviera de Exportacion (Spain)

Naviera Pinillos (Spain)*

Navigazione Generale Italiana (NGI) (Italy)*

Navigazione Libera Triestina (Italy)

Navigazione sul Lago di Garda (Italy)

Nederland Line (Holland)

Nederlandse Tank & Paketvaart Maats (Holland)

Nelson Line (GB)*

Neptun Dampfs. (Germany)

New Bedford, Martha?s Vineyard etc (USA)

New Medway Steam Packet Co (GB)

New Palace Steamers (GB)

New York & Cuba Mail (USA)*

New York & Porto Rico SS Co (USA)*

New Zealand Shipping Co. £7

New Zealand Shipping Co (GB)

Niagara Navigation Co (Canada)

Nicholson Erie-Dover Line (Canada)

Niederland Dampfs. Rhederei (Holland)

Nihonkai Kisen Kaisha (Japan)

Nippon Enkai Ferry (Japan)

Nippon Yusen Kaisha (Japan)*

Nobiling, Reederei, (Germany)

Nomikos Lines (Greece)

Norddeutscher Lloyd (Germany)**

Nordenfjeldske Damps. (Norway)

Nordsee Linie (Germany)

Norfolk & Washington Steamboat Co (USA)

Norske Amerikalinje £12

Norske Amerikalinje (Norway)*

North Coast Steam Navigation Co (Australia)

North of Scotland, Orkney & Shetland Shipping (GB)*

Northern Michigan Transportation (USA)

New Palace Steamers £7

Northern Navigation Co (Canada)

Northern Steamship Co (New Zealand)

Northland Shipping Co (Canada)

Northland Steamship Co (USA)

Norwegian Asia Line (Norway)

Norwegian Caribbean Lines (Norway)

Ocean Steamship Co of Savannah (USA)

Oceanic Steamship Co (USA)

P&O £5

Pacific Far East Line (USA)

Pacific Mail Line (USA)

Oceanic Steamship Co. £12

Old Bay Line (USA)

Old Dominion Line (USA)*

Oldenburg-Portugiesische Damps (Germany)

Olsen, Fred., & Co (Norway)*

Olympic Cruises (Greece)

Orient Lines (GB)

Orient Overseas Line (Hong Kong)

Orient Steam Navigation (GB)

Orient-Pacific Line (GB)

Orient-Royal Mail Line (GB)

Orkney Islands Shipping Co (GB)

Osaka Shosen Kaisha (Japan)**

Ostasiatiske Kompagni (Denmark)

Ostend-Dover Line (Belgium)

Ozean Linie (Germany)*

P&O (GB)

P&O Branch Service (GB)

PAAK (Pakistan)

Pacific Coast Steamships (USA)

Pacific Mail Line £15

Pacific Shipowners

Pacific Steam Navigation Co (GB)**

Pacific Steamship Co (Admiral Line) (USA)

Pacific Transport Line (USA)

Palm Line (GB)*

Panama Mail Steamship (USA)

Panama Railroad (USA)*

Panama Steamship Line (USA)*

Panama-Pacific Line (USA)

Pan-Islamic Steamship Co (Pakistan)*

Peninsular & Occidental Steamship (P&O) (USA)

Peninsular & Oriental Steam Navigation (P&O) (GB)

Plant Line (Canada)*

Polish Ocean Lines (Poland)

Polish-British Steamship Co (Poland)*

Polytechnic Cruising Association (GB)*

Port Jackson & Manly Steamship Co (Australia)

Port Line (GB)

Porto Rico Line (USA)*

Poseidon Schiffahrt (Germany)

Powell Line (GB)*

Presthus Rederi, Johs., (Norway)

Primorsk Shipping Co (USSR)

Prince Line (GB)

Princess Cruise Lines (USA)

Prinzenlinien (Germany)

Provinciale Stoomboot (Holland)

Prudential Lines (USA)

Puget Sound Line (USA)

Purfina (France)

Quebec Steamship (GB)**

Queensboro & Flushing Line (Holland)

R&O Navigation (Canada)

Ragne, Rederiaktiebolaget, (Sweden)

Rankine Line (GB)**

Red Funnel Line (GB)*

Red Funnel £12

Red Star Line (Belgium/USA)*

Regency Cruises

Rennie Line (GB)*

Reut, Rederi AB, (Sweden)

Rickmers Linie (Germany)*

Ropner & Co (GB)

Rennie Line £20

Roumanian State Service (Roumania)**

Royal Cruise Line (Greece)

Royal Hungarian River & Sea Navigation (Hungary)*

Royal Line (Canada)

Royal Mail Steam Packet/Lines (GB)

Royal Netherlands West-India Mail (Holland)**

Royal Viking Line (Norway)
Russian Volunteer Fleet **

Russian Steam Navigation & Trade (Russia)**

Russian-American Line (Russia)*

Sachsisch-Bohmischen Dampfs. Ges (Germany)

Sacor Maritima (Portugal)

Salenrederierma (Sweden)

Saltash, Three Towns & District Steamboat

Salter (GB)

San Francisco & Portland Steamship (USA)

Saturnus, Rederi, (Sweden)

Savannah Line (USA)

Scandinavian American Line (Denmark)*

Schuppe, Victor, Reederei, (Germany)

Scottish Shire Line (GB)*

Seas Shipping (USA)

Sessan Line (Sweden)

Setsuyo Shosen Kaisha (Japan)

SGTM (France)

Shaw, Savill & Albion Co (GB)

Shaw Savill & Albion Line £5

Shin Nihonkai (Japan)

Sidarma Line (Italy)

Silja Line (Scandinavia)

Silver Star Line (USA)**

Siosa Line (Italy)

SITMAR (Soc. Italiana de Services) (Italy)*

Sitmar Line (Italy)

Skou, Ove, (Denmark)

Sloan & Co (GB)*

Smit, L., & Co's Internationale Sleepdienst (Holland)

Soc. 'Italia' (Italy)

Soc. Algerienne de Navigation (France)

Soc. di Navigazione 'Puglia' (Italy)*

Soc. di Navigazione 'San Marco' (Italy)*

Soc. di Navigazione 'Sicilia' (Italy)

Soc. di Navigazione a Vapore Italia (Italy)*

Soc. di Navigazione per Azione 'Italnavi' (Italy)

Soc. Generale de Transports Maritimes (France)

Soc. Geral de Comercio (Portugal)

Soc. Italiana de Servicei (Italy)

Soc. Italiana Servizi Maritime (Italy)

Soc. les Affreteurs Reunis (France)*

Soc. Maritime Nationale (France)

Soc. Misr de Navigation (Egypt)*

Soc. Napoletana di Navigazione e Vapore (Italy)

Soc. Navale de l'Ouest (Fr)

Soc. Partenopea di Navigazione (Italy)

Soc. per Azione di Navigazione 'Italia' (Italy)

Soc. per Azioni di Navigazione 'Tirrenia' (Italy)

Somerfin Passenger Lines (Israel)

South American Saint Line (GB)

Southampton, Isle of Wight & South of England SP (GB)*

Southern Pacific Railroad (USA)

Southern Pacific Steamship (USA)

Soviet Danube Steamship Line (USSR)

St. Petersburg Express Line (Russia)**

Stag Line (GB)

Standard Fruit & Steamship Co (USA)

State Shipping Service (Australia)

States Steamship Co (USA)

Stena Line (Sweden)

Stettiner Damfercompagnie (Germany)

Stinnes, Hugo, (Germany)*

Stockholms Rederi AB Svea (Sweden)

Sudan Government Steamers (Sudan)*

Sun Line (Greece)

Sun Tugs (GB)

Svea Line (Sweden)

Svenska Amerika Line (Sweden)

Svenska Lloyd (Sweden)

Svenska Ameriika Line £6

Svenska Orient Linien (Sweden)

Svenska Rederiaktiebolaget Oresund (Sweden)

Swadeshi Steam Navigation Co (India)**

Swedish-Chicago Line (Sweden)

Taiyo Ferry KK (Japan)

Tasmanian Steamers (Australia)

Taya Line (Spain)**

Tedcastle, McCormick & Co (GB)**

Terukuni Kaiun Kaisha (Japan)

Testa, Bernadino, (Italy)

Thorden Line (Sweden)

Thule Line (Sweden)

Tintore Line (Spain)**

Tirrenia Line (Italy)

Toho Kaiun Kaisha (Japan)

Tokai Line (Japan)

Tor Line (Sweden)

Torm Lines (Denmark)

Townsend Bros. Ferries (GB)

Toyas, John, (Greece)**

Toyo Kisen Kaisha (Japan)

Toyo Yusen (Japan)

Transatlantic, Rederiaktiebolaget, (Sweden)

Transatlantica Italiana (Italy)**

Transatlantica Italiana £12

Transmarin Aktiebolaget (Sweden)

Transports Maritimes Est-Tunisien (France)

Traunsee Dampfschiffahrt (Austria)

Trinder, Anderson & Co (GB)

Turbine Steamers Ltd (GB)

Turkish Maritime Lines (Turkey)

Turnbull, Martin & Co (GB)

Turnbull, Scott & Co (GB)

Tyne General Ferry Co (GB)*

Tyne-Tees Shipping Co (GB)*

Typaldos Lines (Greece)*

Ullswater Navigation & Transit Co (GB)

Union Steam Ship(GB)**

Union Steamship Co (Canada)

Union Steamship Co of New Zealand (GB/NZ)*

Union Sulphur Co (USA)

Union-Castle Line (GB)**

Union Castle Line £10

United American Lines (USA)

United Arab Maritime Co (Egypt)

United Baltic Lines (GB)

United Fruit Lines (USA)

United States Forces (USA)

United States Lines (USA)

Uranium Steamship Co (GB)**

USSR State Shipping Companies, Morflot etc (USSR)

Vaccaro Line (USA)

Van Nievelt, Goudriaan & Co (Holland)

Van Ommeren, Phs., NV (Holland)

Vereeigde Nederlandsche Scheepvaart
(Holland)

Vierwaldstatersee (Switzeralnd)

Viking Cruises (Italy)

Viking Cruising Co (CD)*

Villain & Faosio (Italy)*

Virginia Ferry (USA)

Volga Steam Navigation Co (Russia)

Vriesvaart Maats. (Holland)

Wagenborg's Scheep. (Holland)

Walleniusrederierna (Sweden)

Ward Line (USA)*

Warnemunde-Gedser Linie (Germany)

Warren Line (GB)**

Waterman Steamship Corporation (USA)

Watts, Watts & Co (GB)

Waxholms Nya Angf. (Sweden)

West Line (USA)

White Star Line (GB)**

Wilhelmsen Lines (Norway)

Williamson's Turbine Steamers (GB)

Wilson Line (GB)**

Woermann Linie (Germany)*

Ybarra & Cia (Spain)*

Yeoward Line (GB)*

Zeeland Line (Holland)

Zim Israel Lines (Israel)

Zim Israel Lines £5

FAMOUS LINERS
Lusitania R.M.S.

Sketches of Disaster	£8
Art/Photographic	£6-15
In Memoriam	£15

Celebrated Liners/Tuck R.

Oilette Series/20+ Sets	£6-12

Miscellaneous Liners
Pre-1939

/Coloured	£5-20
/Real Photographic	£4-15
1940 onwards	£4-10
Interiors	£3-10
Hoffman C./Southampton	£5-10
F.G.O. Stuart	£5-10

Titanic R.M.S.

Building/Harland & Woolf	£100+
Ship's anchor in transport	£100+
Leaving Southampton 1912	£90+
Passengers in `Carpathia' lifeboats	£150+
Other related pre-disaster cards	£90+
'Nearer my God to Thee'/Set 3/4.	
Pub. Bamforth. Price per card	£20

The cards listed above are all genuine `Titanic' and mainly real photographic in style. As such they are worth considerably more than other `Titanic' cards listed below, which are usually re-titled versions of her sister ship `Olympic', often overprinted with details of the disaster. The reason for this is that the `Titanic' went down before the majority of publishers got round to photographing her, so they substituted existing pictures of the almost identical `Olympic'. One can tell the difference in that the real `Titanic' had a closed superstructure while that on the `Olympic' was open.

In Memoriam/Bragg E.A.	£50
National Series	£50
RP/Printed Photographic	£35+
Art Types	£30+

Associated Ships

Britannic (Sister ship/4 funnels)	£40
Carpathia	£50
Olympic	£15-35

MISCELLANEOUS PHOTOGRAPHIC

Cable Ships	£5-10
Cargo Ships	£5-15
Cruise Ships	£1-6
Hospital Ships	£12-30

Houseboats	£5
Icebreakers	£10-15
Launchings	£15-30
Lightships	£12-5
On-board-ship scenes	£-10
Pleasure Boats	£3-7
Speedboats	£8-12
Tankers	£3-12
Troopships	£8-12

Convict Ships

At named locations	£15
Unlocated	£6
Interior Studies	£5

Divers

Naval	£5-15
Civilian	£15
Winchester Diver	£18

Docks/Harbours/Ports

Construction/Southampton	£40
Construction/Immingham	£20
Spectacular RP Views	£30
General scenes	£3-10

Ferries

Cross Channel	£3-10
Steam Ferries	£3-10
Floating Bridges	£8
Rowing Boats	£5

Lifeboats

`Inland Launchings'	£35
Advertising Posters RNLI	£35
Lifeboat Saturday Parades	£35
Close-up Studies	£20
Crews/Portraits	£18
Parades	£28
Coastguards/Stations	£10

Lighthouses

GB Locations	£2-10
Foreign Locations	£3-5

Paddle Steamers

GB	£4-15
Overseas	£4-10
Rhine Steamers	£3-10
Swiss Lake Steamers	£2-5

Royal Yachts

GB	£2-5
Foreign	£2-8

Sailing Ships

Barges	£5-15
Coastal	£5-10
Ocean	£5-10

Shipyards

Cammell Laird	£8+
Harland & Woolf	£5-10
Ship under construction	£10-20
Yards miscellaneous	£5-20

Tugs

Paddle	£7-12
Officials	£8-20
Others	£5-10

Whaling Industry

Hebrides/Factory scenes	£45
Ships/General Views	£10-25
Stations/Factory Scene	£25
Washed up/Stranded	£5-18
Ships	£18

Wrecks

HMS Montagu	£5-25
Submarine at Hastings	£10-15
SS Mahratta	£5-15
Other Wrecks	£10-20

Yachts

Americas Cup	£5-10
Racing	£2-6
Private/Powered	£6

Celtic Glen R/P £7

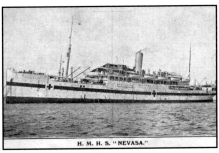

Hospital Ship Pr. £12

SILK CARDS

The earliest cards of this type were Woven Silks which originated in Germany in 1898. The main manufacturers were H.M. Krieger and Rudolf Knuffman. Shortly afterwards in 1903 the Coventry based firms of Thomas Stevens and W.H. Grant began making similar cards in this country, while at around the same time Neyret Frores commenced manufacturing Woven Silks in France.

Embroidered Silks first appeared in 1900, although it was not until the First World War that they reached the height of their popularity. The basic difference between the two types is that Woven Silks were machine made, and consequently of uniform finish, whereas Embroidered silks were mainly produced on hand looms, leaving a raised surface where the threads may be clearly seen, with often irregular variations in design from card to card.

The RF Catalogue 1985 contains a comprehensive listing by Chris Radley of all the main Woven and Embroidered Silk card types.

Market Report

This is a specialized market where prices are volatile and prices tend to be determined at auction for the rarer types. Condition is paramount. There is a steady demand for WW1 patriotic examples from the general antique trade at current price levels.

WOVEN

STEVENS T.

Experimental Types	£90
Portraits	£60+
Religious Subjects	£50
Views	£25+
General Subjects	£25+

Ships

Titanic	£750
Battleships	£90+
Transports	£60
Liners, Steamers and Landing Stages	£40+
Hands Across the Sea	£30+

Above; Woven Silk, Military £50

Alpha Series
(Designs produced by Stevens for Alpha Publishing Co.)

Greetings	£25
Flags	£25+
Stevens Designs	£30+

GRANT W.H.

Exhibitions	£40+
Portraits	£40+
Subjects	£35+
Hands Across the Sea / Ships and Greetings	£35+
Greetings from	£30+
Greetings, Songs and Hymns	£35
Views	£20+

Hands Across the Sea £40

Above; 'Flame' £20

FRANCE
A. Benoiston

Paris Exposition 1900	£150
Others	£40

Neyret Freres
1903-1904

Art Nouveau/Paintings/Portraits	£50+

1905-1914

Art Nouveau/Portraits/Views	£50+

1907-1918

Religion/Paintings	£30+

1915-1917

WW1 Patriotic/Portraits	£25+

1917-1918

WW1 Patriotic/Portraits	£25+

1916-1919

Flames	£20+

1917-1918

Sentimental Greetings	£25

Bertrand and Boiron 1915-1916

WW1 Portraits/Religion	£50+
Others 1930-1945	£12+

GERMANY

H.M. Kreiger	£30+
Rudolf Knuffman/1898-1905	£30+
Nazi Interest/1936-1938	£50+
Others/1899-1915	£25+

OTHER EUROPEAN

Austria/1900-1939	£25+
Switzerland/1900-1910	£25+
Czechoslovakia/1916-1938	£12+

JAPAN

Views and Portraits	£40
With Copy of Grant Mount	£50

U.S.A.

1904 Exposition	£200
Set 14	£2000
Others	£30+

PRINTED SILK/SATIN

Flames//Edition Gabriel	£20
Kitchener Lord	£20
Stewart & Woolf Series	£15
Regiments/Countries	£15
Miscellaneous	£8

H.M. Krieger

Four Seasons Set	£200
Others	£30

Cavell Edith

In original D.M. envelope	£6
Card only	£4

Cinema Stars/Plain Backs

Transatlantic Films	£3

FAB PATCHWORK CARDS
W.N. SHARPE/BRADFORD
Actresses	£15
Royalty	£15
Views	£12
Heraldic	£12
Flowers	£12
PAT.735 (Gaunt Armley)	£12

EMBROIDERED/WW1
REGIMENTAL BADGES
Household Cavalry	£40
Cavalry of the Line	£60
Cavalry Special Reserve Units	£60
Yeomanry Regiments	£60
Royal Regiment of Artillery	
British Regiments	£35
Overseas Regiments	£50
Foot Guards	£50
Infantry of the Line	£50
Territorial Force	
Independent Units	£50
London Regiments	£40
Expeditionary Forces	
Britain/France	£40
Australasia	£40
Canada/USA	£50
Divisional Corps	£40
British Army Corps	
British Corps/ASC.RE.RFA, etc.	£12
Overseas Corps	£40
Overseas Regiments	£75
Royal Navy	
Units	£50
Ships	£50
Royal Navy	£35
Royal Naval Air Service	£50
Royal Air Force	
Royal Flying Corps	£40
Royal Air Force	£40
Independent Organisations	
Red Cross/Salvation Army etc.	£50

The whole field of WW1 Embroidered Silk Cards is vast and complex, with literally thousands of different designs covered under the three columns of this listing. Many of these cards are very scarce, in some cases only one copy being known. This catalogue can only offer a general guide to type and price.

The Queens Royal West Surrey Regiment £50

LEADERS/STATESMEN/ROYALTY
Inset Photos/Single	£20
Inset Photos/Doubles	£25
Names/WW1 Leaders	£25

HERALDIC
Overseas Towns	£40
Overseas Countries/Islands	£25
European Towns	£15
European Countries	£15
English Towns	£30
England/Scotland/Wales	£25
Ireland/Eire/Shamrock Isle	£25

Birn Brothers/With Printed Title
Overseas Towns	£25
European Towns	£20
English Towns	£20

YEAR DATES
1914-1919	£10
1920-1923	£15
1925-1939	£18
1940	£10
1945	£15

SENTIMENTAL GREETINGS/
HEARTS & FLOWERS TYPE

Flag/Patriotic	£8
Sentimental Greetings	£5

Many cards of this type were made in the form of an Envelope. If such a card still contains its original insert, the following premium may be added to the prices above:

Silk Handkerchief	£3
Artist signed	£1
Celluloid	£1
War Scenes	£1
Perfumed	£1

BETTER DESIGNS

Advertising	£40
Aircraft/Guns etc.	£15
Army Camps	£25
Buildings	£20
Cartoons	£18
Cathedrals	£20
Cathedrals in Flames	£15
Cats	£15
Colonial Exhibition	£40
English Buildings	£30
Father Xmas/Girls etc	£25
Flower Baskets	£8
Pan-Pacific Exhibition 1915	£40
Personal Names	£15
Saints	£15
Soldiers/Sailors/Medals etc	£25
War Destruction	£15
Zeppelins	£20

To qualify for listed price the image must be the dominant feature of the card. A tiny Cat or small Building will not do!

EMBROIDERED/
MISCELLANEOUS

Birn Bros.

Printed Regimental Badges	£20
Flowers	£8

Tuck R. & Sons

Broderie D'Art series   £6

Spanish Embroidery

Early cards	£6
Later	£3
Modern	£1.50

Royal Naval Air Service £35

Year Dates 1917 £10

Salvation Army £50

157

SPORT

One of the subjects which enjoys a popularity today at least equal to that of the Edwardian period, when Sporting cards filled every album. Always a good collecting area with a very wide variety of cards, where prices have been subject to continued and steady growth over the years.

Market Report

Quality and unusual cards representing the major modern sports have continued to perform well, but the more common cards in all subjects remain static. The rarer photographic cards in these areas are fetching premium prices.

Price growth in Stadiums, Swimming, Olympic, Named golf, Rugby, Motor Sport, Cycling.

ANGLING
Comic Sketches	£3
Miscellaneous	£4

ARCHERY
Competitions	£10
Miscellaneous	£5

ATHLETICS
Meetings	£15
Athletes/Named	£15
Stadiums	£12

BADMINTON
Miscellaneous	£8

BASEBALL
Players	£5/£15
Comic Sketches	£10/£18
Stadiums	£5/ £12

BASKETBALL/NETBALL
Miscellaneous	£4

BILLIARDS/SNOOKER
Players/Named Photographic Pro	£45
Players/General	£10
Billiard Halls	£8-£15
Comic Sketches	£8/12

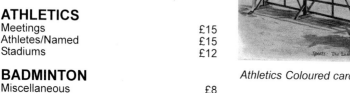

Athletics Coloured card £15

BOARD GAMES
Chess	£15
Other games	£3

BOWLS
Miscellaneous	£4

BOXING
Famous Boxers/Beagles Ltd.	£15
Professional Boxing	£12-£20
Jack Johnson	£25
Amateur Boxing	£5

Photographic local billiards champion Amateur £10

FLOYD PATTERSON

Boxing, Floyd Patterson, £15

BULLFIGHTING
Art Studies   £2
Photographic   £3

CAVES/CAVING
Miscellaneous   £2

CRICKET
Players   £15
W.G.Grace   £30
Donald Bradman   £25
County Grounds   £15
Comic Sketches   £8/£15
Teams
County Teams   £15-20
International Teams   £15-20
Star Series   £6
National Series   £15
Amateur Teams/ Identified   £4

CROQUET
Miscellaneous   £6

CURLING
Miscellaneous   £3

CYCLE RACING
Tour de France/Portraits   £20
Tour de France/Pre 1939   £25
Personalities/Events/Pre 1939   £20
   /Post 1939   £10

FENCING
Miscellaneous   £6

FOOTBALL
LEAGUE TEAMS
Series
Rapid Photographic series   £50
Famous Football Teams/
Wrench Series 107...(Names)   £50
Oxo Advertising Cards   £50
London Football Teams/
B&B Series G11/Coloured   £40
Ozograph Series/Bristol   £40
Rotary Photographic/Series 3844   £50
Health & Strength   £40
Misch & Co "Football Teams"   £40

Miscellaneous
Football League/Bw photographic   £45-60
   /Bw printed   £40-50
Olympic Teams   £15/£30
Prices for League Teams are governed
largely by the status of the team itself.
e.g. Man. Utd. is worth more than Barnsley.

Players
Wrench Series 21../29../c.1903   £45

Steve Bloomer commemorative card,
facsimile autograph. Rare card £45+

Benefit Cards/Football League   £30-£45
Bw photographic   £35
Tuck Famous football players   £40
Birmingham Novelty Co 'Football' series   £50
C.W.Faulkner &co   £45
"Herriot" series   £45

MISCELLANEOUS
Wembley Cup Final 1923/Campbell Gray/
Commemorative Set 3/With Packet   £140
   /Without packet   £80
Arsenal Cartoon/Kentish Independent   £45
International Teams   £40
Football Series 940/c.1903
Tuck R. & Sons   £40
In Memoriam Cards/In Memory of/
b/w Comic Sketches   £30

Newcastle United, later period team group £35

Hampstead Football Ground.

Non-league Stadiums similar to this fetch £20

Football League Stadiums	£45-£75
Football Stadiums Overseas	£15
Football Colours/Frank Reynolds/	
Comic Sketches	£15
Non-League Teams/Semi-Pro	£15
Amateur Teams/Identified	£6
/Unidentified	£4
Crowd scenes/Brighton/F. Wiles	£12
/Miscellaneous	£10
Comic Sketches	£8

GOLF

Wrench Series/Players/	
Bw undivided back	£150+
Players/Named	£100+
Pro Tournaments	£120+
Club Houses	£8/£15
Championship Courses	£15-£25
Courses	£5/£8
Comic Sketches	£8/£15

12 FRINTON-ON-SEA. — The Golf Club. — LL.

Golf club houses, £12 would be par for the course for close up views similar to this.

Advert Cards

Poster Type	£50
Product Advertising	£30

GYMNASTICS

Miscellaneous	£3

HOCKEY

International teams	£12
Miscellaneous	£3-£8

Hockey player £8

HORSE SHOWS/JUMPING

Int. Horse Show/Product Advert	£8
Show Jumping/Riders	£5
General Scenes	£3

RACECOURSE, NEWMARKET.

Horse Racing, Newmarket Racecourse is one of the more common, but an early card like this is still a good bet at £7.50

HORSE RACING

Jockeys	£8-15
Race Horses	£7.50

Race Courses

Doncaster/York etc./	
Printed multi-view type	£4
In current use	£6-£8

Pre-1939

Gatwick	£70
Lewes	£50
RP studies	£20

Printed/Goodwood etc. £8
Abandoned £15
Courses where Racing was abandoned long ago are worth more than those in current use.

Series

B & D/Kromo Series	£12
Bird H./Everett's Series	£12
Meissner & Buch Series 1003	£15
Tuck R./Derby Winners	£15
Tuck R./Popular Racing Colours	£15
Walker J./Celebrated Racers	£15
Wildt & Kray/Racing Colours	£15
Wrench Series	£15

MOTOR RACING

L'Hirondelle Series	£20
Peking-Paris	£15
French Drivers c.1905/	
Pub. J. Bouveret/Le Mans	£15
European Circuits	£8
Valentine's R/P racing car series	£7

Brooklands

Action/Portraits	£20
Track Construction	£20

Gordon Bennett Races

Coloured	£18
RP/Printed	£10

Isle of Man

Motor Cars/RP Close-up	£50
Action/RP Middle distance	£25

Valentine & Sons

Autocar Series	£8

Action/Portraits

Pre-1939	£15
1940 onwards	£7
Art Studies	£7

MOTOR CYCLE RACING
Isle of Man

Pre-1939	£25
1940 onwards	£12

Racing/Other Circuits

Pre-1939	£18
1940 onwards	£10

Action/Portraits

Pre-1939	£18
1940 onwards	£8

MOUNTAINEERING

Everest	£10
Miscellaneous	£3

Motor Cycle Racing, Colour £18

The SUPREME SUNBEAM

Land speed record, Sunbeam £15

OLYMPIC GAMES
SUMMER GAMES

1896 Athens	£10/£80
1900/04/08 Expos	£1/£8
1906 Athens	£1/£60
1912 Stockholm	£5/£30
1920 Antwerp	£8/£40
1924 Paris	£8/£30
1928/1956	£2/£15

1912, Football at the Olympics in Stockholm £25 will be a winning price

1960/1968	£2/£7
1972/1988	£1/£7
1992/2012	£1/£2

WINTER GAMES
1924/1928	£10/£50
1932/1936	£3/£12
1948/1956	£3/£10
1960/1968	£2/£8
1972/1988	£1/£2
Ancient Olympia	£2
Empty Stadiums	£1/£2
Crowded Stadiums	£3/£7
Torch Ceremony	£2/£5

POLO
| Miscellaneous | £3 |

ROWING
Named Crews	£6
Oxford Eights etc.	£6
Henley Regatta	£4

RUGBY FOOTBALL
International Teams	£20/£25
Rugby League professional teams	£15/£30
Rugby Union - major teams	£35
League/Union Teams	£30
Players/Named	£25
Amateur teams, local (both codes)	£6/£10
South African comic cards of internationals in UK 1907	£25

SAILING/YACHTING
Admiral's Cup	£5
Racing	£5
Kirk of Cowes/RP studies	£5
Powered Yachts	£5
General scenes	£3

SHOOTING
| Scenes | £12 |
| General Shooting | £5-£8 |

SKATING / RINKING
| Miscellaneous | £3 |
| Professional | £5 |

Top quality photographic Speedway stars, £18

SPEEDWAY
| Riders/Pre-1939 | £18 |
| Riders/Post-War | £12 |

SPORTS DAY/LOCAL SPORTS
| Miscellaneous | £6 |

STADIA
British Football League	£45-£75
Overseas Football grounds	£5-£15
Amateur Grounds	£10-£20
Athletic Tracks UK	£15-£25
Athletic Tracks Overseas	£8

New Zealand International Rugby team , £25

Sheffield Wednesday FC R/P   £75

SWIMMING

Channel	£15
Portraits of famous swimmers	£12
Miscellaneous	£6/12
Life Saving	£8/£20

TABLE TENNIS

Players/Competition	£25
Players/General	£8
Comic/Early	£25
Comic Sketches	£15

TENNIS

Wimbledon scenes (early)	£18
Wimbledon scenes	£12
Tournaments/Miscellaneous	£8/£15
Courts	£5
Comic Sketches	£7/£15

Players

Portraits/Chaplain Jones	£20
Portraits/E.A. Trim early period	£18
Portraits/E.A. Trim pre 1939	£15
Competition/Pre-1939	£15
/1940 on	£8
Wimbledon series/c.1960	£5

WALKING

London-Brighton	£10
Other Races	£6
Comic	£3
Mountain Walking	£1

WATER POLO

Miscellaneous	£8

WINTER SPORTS

Skating	£3
Skiing	£3
Tobogganing	£2
Art types	£4

WRESTLING/BODY BUILDING

Advertising poster type	£20-£25
Miscellaneous	£12/£20
Sandow	£15-£20
Hackenschmidt	£12-£15
Gymnasiums	£6-£12
Photographic Body Builders	£12

Tennis, Comic sketches, £10

Body Building and fitness advertising is always of interest £25

THEATRICAL

Part of the staple of the old publishers. Theatrical cards of all kinds filled the Edwardian albums, and have retained their popularity to the present day.

Market Report

Supplies are plentiful of Edwardian theatrical stars which are keeping prices down to around £1 for a large proportion of these cards. Unusual Music Hall acts are worth looking out for.

ACTORS/ACTRESSES

Baker, Josephine	£60
Bernhardt, Sarah	£6
Coward, Noel	£15
Duncan, Isadora	£20
Hari, Mata	£30
Irving Henry/Memorial Card	£6
Langtry, Lily	£8
Portraits/Miscellaneous	£1.50
Play Scenes	£1.50
Embossed/Applique	£1.50

The predominant theme in this category is Edwardian Actors and Actresses of which vast quantities exist. Formerly little collected, they have now started to attract buyers, often looking for one or two named stars.

In the circumstances a price of £1.50 is considered reasonable for one card, but they can be picked up in bulk at auction, or from a dealer, at less than this figure.

ADVERTISING
POSTER TYPE

Coloured	£15+
Black & White	£6

Good quality poster adverts like this one could sell for £20

Miscellaneous

Comedians/Performers	£5
Playbill Reproductions	£10
Play Scenes/With Advert	£3

Where applicable, the value of Poster Type cards is determined by the name of the Artist. See main Artist Index.

Ballet Dancer Anna Pavlova £15

BALLET
Artistes

Fonteyn, Margot	£10
Genee, Dame Adelina	£10
Markova, Alicia	£10
Nijinsky	£50
Nureyev, R	£22
Pavlova	£15
Other Artists	£6
Companies/Troupes	£6
Post-war	£3

THEATRES

Music Hall/Variety	£25
Opera Houses	£4
Piers/Winter Gardens	£3
Interiors	£4
London West End/Coloured	£4

Prices for Theatres are for good, close-up mainly photographic studies and not for middle or far-distance views. Theatres forming part of a standard Street Scene are classed in that category

Harry Lauder comic   £6

sic Hall
formers

Contortionists £20

Variety artist, Eugene Stratton £8

Circus artist, Anita the Midget £12

Circus clowns £15

Circus or fairground motorcycle stunt acts £20

CIRCUS

ADVERTISING

Barnum & Bailey
Poster Type	£40
Others	£20

Buffalo Bill's Wild West
Poster Type	£25
Others	£15

Miscellaneous
Poster Types	£30
Others	£15

MISCELLANEOUS
Acts/Performers	£8
Animals Caged	£6
Bands	£8
Circus Sites/Identified G.B.	£40

Clowns
Early/Chromo Litho	£20
Photographic Performers	£15

Freaks
Animal	£10
Human	£6-£12
Giants	£6-£12
Midgets/Troupes	£6-£12

VARIETY ARTISTS
Bard, Wilkie	£6
Chevalier, Albert	£6
Chirgwin	£8
Elliott, G.H.	£8
Forde, Florrie	£6
Formby, George	£12
King, Hetty	£6
Lauder, Harry	£6
/Comic	£6
Leno Dan	£6
Lloyd Marie	£9
Miller, Max	£10
Robey, George	£4
Stratton, Eugene	£8
Tate, Harry	£6
Tich, Little	£8
Tilley. `Vesta	£5

RADIO/TELEVISION
Children's Programmes/Radio	£6
Radio Celebrities	£4
Studios	£6
Transmitting Stations	£5
Wireless Sets	£8
QSL Cards/Radio Amateurs	£1
Comic Sketches	£6
Children's TV/Sooty etc.	£3
Brooke Bond Chimps	£3
Radio Pictorial Series	£5

MISCELLANEOUS
Amateur Dramatics	£1.50
Escapologists/Stuntmen	£20
Harry Houdini	£100+
Magicians/Conjurers	£25
Speciality Acts	£6
Ventriloquists	£25
Drag Artists	£4

Autographs
Known Stars	£3+
Unkown Artists	£1

Prices quoted are for Autographs signed in ink. Printed Autographs have no value above that of the subject.

Cabaret
French Skeletons	£1
Other Acts	£3

Concert Parties
Named Troupes	£4
Un-named	£1.50

Dancing
Ballroom/Stage etc.	£2
Greetings/Romance	£2

French Showgirls
`A Travers Les Coulisses'	£12
Moulin Rouge/Coloured	£12
Portraits/Miscellaneous	£3

Midget. £12 This photo postcard shows George Kibbey, aged 17, Height 33 inches, weight 57lbs

TOPOGRAPHICAL

Arlesey REAL PHOTO £35

The most popular and eagerly sought after cards in the hobby, the finest of which have again seen a dramatic rise in price. Yet herein lies the enigma of Topographical cards, because it could be argued that the great majority of them are virtually unsaleable! As has often been said before, the problem with Topographical cards is that there are a great many very common cards of any particular area. These include the standard High Street views, local buildings of interest, the church and the park etc.; originally produced in vast quantities by regional and national publishers. And once the collector has obtained these common views he does not buy them again. They remain in the box, as any postcard dealer will testify, for possibly years! And being so common they keep turning up over and over again in the dealer's current buying. I would estimate that it would take an enthusiastic collector no more than six months to assemble a good collection of common cards such as these. But then he joins the rest of us in seeking the more elusive, and far more interesting back streets and scenes of local social history interest e.g. the Railway Station, Cinema, Theatre, Shop Fronts, Delivery Vehicles, Fairgrounds, Trams, Buses, Fires, Floods, Disasters, Post Offices, Public Houses, Windmills, Local Events etc. But these cards by their very nature were invariably produced in relatively small quantities by the local photographer, and today, some ninety years later, allowing for natural wastage, they are extremely thin on the ground. So as ever more collectors come to the hobby, all of them searching for these better cards, the prices go up and will continue to go up. It is an oft-repeated maxim in the postcard trade that you can sell cards like these but you cannot buy them! Indeed many of the really superb street scenes are now so highly saleable that they often don't get as far as the dealer's box or album, but are offered privately to the collector of that particular town at a negotiated price!

So this is the Topographical market we are at present faced with. There is nothing we can do about it, save to re-double our efforts to find the cards which collectors want.

If I may now look briefly at the production of Topographical cards and at the methods involved, the following notes may be of interest to collectors. These are based on a paper written by JHD Smith in conjunction with Brian Lund, which was published in `Picture Postcard Monthly' in June 1982. They looked at the accepted definitions of `Real Photographic' and `Printed' cards, and suggested a more clearly defined structure, offering some thoughts toward a re-assessment of the Topographical nomenclature. To briefly summarise our conclusions, they were as follows:

Post Office Corner, Hindhead R/P £35

POSTCARDS WERE FINISHED IN TWO BASICALLY DIFFERENT METHODS:

1. By a photographic process.   **2. By a Printing Machine process.**

PHOTOGRAPHIC
Local Photographers

By small, local firms producing each photograph individually, or in very small batches onto an existing postcard back, and hand-cutting or guillotining the batches, possibly four at a time. The style of finish varies widely, from the superb clarity of the very best examples, to the image which has almost faded away, according to the skill of the photographer in the developing process. The caption was often hand-written, with the photographer's name or initials often appearing on the front of the card. These may be styled as the best examples of 'Real Photographic' cards, and the work of photographers such as Bragg, Gibson,

Stratford, East London, Animated Real Photographic process, with transport interest £35

Garratt, Wellsted, Ross, Braddock, Perkins and Daniell, immediately spring to mind as pre-eminent in this field. There are of course many other local photographers who produced superb work, and here there is a great deal of research yet to be done. These men concentrated upon their own immediate locality, and as a result it is in this work that you will find the fascinating cards of local history interest referred to above, and thus it follows that in these cards we are now seeing the most significant advance in price.

Regional Publishers

Postcards were produced in quantity by larger companies who covered a wide circulation area. They probably used a mass-production technique involving contact printing from a negative on to machines which could produce copies in large numbers. Many of these cards are designated 'Real Photographic' on the back, and are often found with a white border framing the picture. They are characterised by a uniform, glossy finish, the machine controlled output being less susceptible to variations in tone. Leading firms who worked in this style include Sankey, Camburn and E.T. Bush, covering the areas of Cumbria, S.E. England and South Wales respectively. The subjects depicted tend to be High Street and main street views, the Railway Station, Cinema, Theatre, Post Office, and other views of immediate local interest, although you will not find cards here, showing a line of barefoot children queueing up at a soup kitchen, this being essentially the province of the local man. Cards in this section do not generally command such high prices, partly because they are more readily available, being produced in larger quantities, and also because the scenes they depict tend to be more 'standard' than the off-beat work of the local photographer.

National Publishers

Also involved in postcard production, but this time on a national scale were big publishing houses such as Frith, Valentine, Davidson Bros, W.H.S. Kingsway Series and many others. Their work was machine produced and similar in all respects to that of the Regional Publishers both in style and content, but the difference lay in the fact that these were national publishing concerns who produced cards covering the length and breadth of the country. Prices here would fall into the same range as those for the Regional Publishers.

PRINTED CARDS

47 ARUNDEL. — Hight Street. — LL.

Printed postcard by LL £12

Without getting into a complex and perhaps misleading explanation of all the different printing techniques employed here, it is enough to state that if a card was not produced by one of the Photographic methods given above, in other words if it does not have a glossy finish, then it must have been produced by one of the many printing processes available at the time. Basically the method employed involved splitting the original photographic image into dots, or what is known as the screen process, and then transferring this on to a printing plate. While this method enabled mass produced copies of quite appalling definition to flood the market, the finest printed cards are the equal of the finest photographics. Here again we have three main areas of commerce.

Local Publishers
Many local photographers produced cards in a variety of printed formats, and some may have combined these with their own original photographic work. Many local shops and stores had their names overprinted on to the backs of cards produced for them by the Regional Publishers. The content of these cards, while being essentially local in character, does fall into the same style as that of the Regional Publishers above, and prices would be at approximately the same levels.

Regional Publishers
The work of Charles Martin in London and the South East perhaps most clearly illustrates the very high standard to which many Regional Publishers aspired. If we may include Lucien Levy also in this classification, some of his work is certainly the equal of anything in the entire Topographical field. Subjects depicted were again similar to those of the Regional Publishers of Photographic cards, the 'line of hungry children' being always the work of what has been termed 'the back-street photographer'. Prices for these cards fall into line with the other regional photographic work above.

National Publishers
Here we come to those cards which today form the great bulk of stock to be found in any dealer's box. Endless mass-produced stereotyped views by Frith, Judges, Valentine, Tuck, Stengel and many other substantial publishing corporations. Printed in a wide variety of styles, with many cards coloured, and nearly all of them depicting the standard views and tourist areas of any town or city, as well as incalculable numbers of Churches, Cathedrals, Seasides, Scottish Lochs and Welsh Mountains! Some, of course, are more interesting than others, but overall, these are the cards which the collector soon obtains. Prices for the majority of them are at the lower end of the price scale.

Market Report
This is the driving force of the entire hobby. It accounts for around 70% of the market in this country. Prices are polarizing due to the emergence of ebay as a main contributory factor in determining price levels. Competition for unusual cards of desirable locations has meant that £100 cards on the internet are an almost daily occurrence while the price of more common views are being forced downwards. All this affects the prices dealers have to pay for their stock and the price collectors are prepared to pay at fairs.

Competition has forced up the prices of aerial views and schools for example but location is all important which is unfortunately outside the scope of this catalogue.

Street Scene R/P £15

London Suburb, superb view £35

VILLAGES

Spectacular animated street scenes	£35+
Animated street scenes	£25
Other street scenes	£15
Empty streets	£6
Common Views/Landscapes	£2
Modern views/1945-1970	£3

COUNTRY TOWNS

Spectacular animated street scenes	£35+
Animated street scenes	£20
Other street scenes	£12
Empty streets	£6
Common views/Town Hall etc.	£2
Modern views/1945-1970	£3

INDUSTRIALISED TOWNS AND CITIES

Spectacular animated street scenes	£30+
Animated street scenes	£20
Other street scenes	£12
Empty streets	£8
Common Views/City Centres etc.	£2
Modern views/1945-1970	£3

LONDON SUBURBAN

Spectacular animated street scenes	£35+
Animated street scenes	£25
Other street scenes	£12
Empty streets	£10
Common Views/Parks etc.	£3
Modern views/1945-1970	£3

LONDON CENTRAL

Spectacular animated street scenes	£20
Animated street scenes	£15
Other street scenes	£8
Empty streets	£6
Oxford St./Regent St. etc.	£1.50
LL Published	£5
Common Views/Trafalgar Square etc.	.50
Modern views/1945-1970	.50

London Central, animated scene R/P £20

Within these classifications many anomalies exist. For example, there are some superb animated LL cards of London Central, which at the same time are very common! With these, and similar examples, only knowledge and experience can be your guide. I have not tried to be too specific and break this down even further into considerations of `RP,

Kingsway Series R/P £12

Printed, Coloured, Local and National Photographers etc., as this would only lead to confusion. I have not even tried to separate Real Photographic from Printed cards because, as we all know, there are some awful RPs, and some very fine Printed types. I have, however, given the main category to those superb Topographical views of both kinds which stand out in any collection.

* Animated Street Scenes: A card which is full of activity, life and movement, or which depicts a scene of particular relevance to that area, or is otherwise of unusual interest. These cards are very much the exception, often being produced by the local photographer. The majority of street scenes in any dealer's stock would be classified as `Other street scenes'.

Eastbourne, Judges Series R/P £6

MISCELLANEOUS

Abbeys/Convents/Priories	£1.50
Aerial Views	£5
Archaeological Sites/Villages	£1.50
Bridges/Viaducts	£4
Castles	£1.50
Cathedrals	£1
Chapels	£3
Churches	£2
Crystal Palace	£3
Follies	£5
Greetings/Town Names	£1.50
Holiday areas	£1
Hotels	£6
Interiors	£1.50
Lake District scenery	£1
Landscapes	£1
Manor Houses	£5
Monuments/Memorials	£3
Multi-view	£4
Municipal Buildings	£3
Parks	£3
Seaside/Common views	.50
Special Events	£20
Stately Homes	£1.50
Much photographed buildings	£1

Withernsea, Yorkshire Pr. £7

Carlisle, Col. Pr. £6

Every dealer will have his own idea of the value of any card backed up by a specialised knowledge of his own area, so at best, the prices above should only be taken as a broad general average, capable of movement up or down as determined by the particular card.

Middleton R/P £6

Ashington R/P £10

New Tea Rooms, Stansted R/P £35

The Village, Formby R/P £15

High Street, Rusthall R/P £35

St. Helen's Pr. £12

Fishponds, Bristol R/P. £40

Denham Village Pr. £12

Sydenham R/P. £30

SOCIAL HISTORY ~ SHOPFRONTS

Superb R/P £35

Butchers Shop R/P £ 40

Redruth R/P £ 20

R/P £ 35

R/P £20

R/P £ 15

SOCIAL HISTORY

This is Topographical by another name and the same comments apply. You can almost name your own price for the better RP studies and the scarce cards of local history interest. At the same time there are a great many interesting cards in this classification which are very reasonably priced.

It is pointed out that for all relevant entries e.g. Fairs . Post Offices . Public Houses .

Street Markets . Windmills etc. the stated priceis a broad average figure for a card, either RP or Printed, fully identified and showing a 'Close-up at a named location', with Real Photographic cards being the most desirable. Unlocated cards and middle or far-distance views would be priced accordingly.

Please see WHAT THE PRICES MEAN on P.30 ***

AGRICULTURE

Agricultural Shows	£15
Carting	£12
Crofters	£6
Dalesmen	£5
Farm Machinery/Tractors etc	£18
Farms	£8
Farmworkers	£6
Flower Picking	£6
Fruit Picking	£6
Herdsmen	£5
Trees	£1.50

Harvesting

Reaping	£5
Threshing machines/Located	£35
/Unlocated	£20
Hay Carts/RP studies	£8
General Harvesting scenes	£3

Hop Picking

Demonstrations in Kent	£75
Real Photographic scenes/Located	£20
/Unlocated	£10

There are many superb RP studies of Hop Picking. Everything depends upon location.

Cooper's Series/Maidstone/RP	£15
The "Kent" Series/Invicta	
Pub: G.A. Cooper/A.N. Hambrook	£8
Young & Cooper/Bw	£8
/Coloured	£4

There are certain Y&C coloured cards which are very common.

Filmer's Home Hop Picking Series	£8
T.A. Flemons/Tonbridge	£8
"Solochrome" Series/E.A. Sweetman	£6
"Solograph" Series/E.A. Sweetman	£6

For Hampshire/Worcestershire etc. follow the price guide above.

Foreign Hop Picking	£5

Lavender Industry

Fields/Growing	£8
Picking	£10
Carting	£35

Ploughing

Oxen in Sussex/RP	£25
/Printed	£8
Plough Horses	£3
Ploughing/General scenes	£2

Sheep

Lambing	£6
Shearing	£12
Sheep Dips	£12
Sheepdog Trials	£12
Shepherds	£6
/South Downs/RP studies	£10

CANALS

Aqueducts/Bridges/Locks	£8
Barges/Close-up	£40
Canal construction/Workers	£40
Disasters	£40
Events/Gatherings, etc.	£40
Military Canals	£3
Tunnels	£8

Hop Picking R/P £10

Narrow Canals

Spectacular Real Photographic	£50
Real Photographic	£10/£16
Coloured/Sepia/BW	£6
Common views/Hythe, Llangollen etc.	£2

Ship Canals

Caledonian/Crinan/Exeter etc.	£2
Manchester Ship Canal	£5

River Navigations

Traffic/Close-up	£15
General views	£6

As with other Subjects, a particularly good card or an unusual view on a seldom photographed Canal, would fetch a price well in excess of these general figures.

COAL MINING

Coal Miners

Groups/Portraits	£20/£30

Collieries

Surface/Close-up	£20/£40
/Middle Distance	£12
Somerset Coalfield	£25
Underground	£10
Models	£6
Pit Girls	£10
Open-cast Mining	£30
Art Type	£2
Coal Picking	£60

Certain views of Collieries in South Wales, published by M.J.R.B. have been remaindered and are therefore worth considerably less than the prices given above.

Judge Shah, R/P £6

Series

Kinsley Evictions 1905	£50

For full details on this series please refer to PPV 2003

M. Brookes/Pontypridd	£10
Cannock Chase	£10
Clay Cross Co./Set 25	£10
Timothy's Series/South Wales	£10
Other series	£10

A number of Collieries produced series of cards depicting work both at the surface and underground.

Disasters

Hamstead Colliery	£15
Senghenydd Colliery	£30
Other Named Events	£25
In Memoriam Cards	£25
In Memoriam Gothard	£20/£75
Rescue Teams	£20

CRIME & PUNISHMENT

Judges/Barristers	£6
Prisons	£5
Prisoners at Work	£5
Warders at Dartmoor	£1.50
Prisoners at Portland	£1.50

CYCLING

Close-up RP studies	£6
Tandems	£10
Tricycles	£15
Military	£5
Greetings/Romantic	£3
Comic Sketches	£3

Advert Cards

Poster Type	£40
Others	£15

See also SPORT

DISASTERS

Coast Erosion/Landslips	£15
/Black Rock/Brighton	£2
Explosions	£20
Floods	£20
Frozen Seas	£6
In Memoriam Cards	£20
Lightning Damage	£18
Snow Damage	£15
Storm Damage	£18
Subsidence	£20
Wrecked Buildings/Piers	£15
War Damage/WW1 Air Raids	
/Ramsgate	£12
/Scarborough	£8
Other locations	£15

Earthquakes

Essex 1884	£8
Other locations/GB	£20
Messina	£1.50
San Francisco	£5
Other locations/Foreign	£3

Events

Faversham 1916/Funeral scenes	£15
Lincoln Typhoid Outbreak 1905	£60
Louth Floods 1920	£18
Lynmouth Floods 1952	£8
Newport Dock 1909	£50
Northwich Subsidence	£12
Norwich Floods	£12
Southend Pier	£10
Vanguard Motor Accident/ Handcross 1906	£10
Weston Super Mare Storm 1903	£12
Worthing Pier	£10

DOMESTIC LIFE

Corkscrews	£8
Knitting	£4
Weddings/Brides/Groups	£2
/Wedding Cakes	£2

Country Houses

Buildings	£4
Domestic Servants	£5
Gardens	£2
Kitchens	£5

Photography

Cameras/Equipment	£8
Greetings/Romantic	£4
Comic Sketches	£6
Stereoscopic cards	£4

These are cards with two adjacent pictures, best viewed through a Stereo viewer for full effect.
There are many different series and subjects.

Telephones

Correspondence cards	£8
Telephone in photograph	£4
Telephone Exchanges/Operators	£20
Greetings/Romantic	£3
Comic Sketches	£2

FAIRS

Amusement Parks	£5
Southend Kursaal	£5
Wall of Death/Action photos	£15
/Arenas	£8
Fetes	£12
Seaside Fairs/Water Chutes	£5

Feats/Wagers

Walking Round the World	£10
/George M. Schilling	£5

/Man in the Iron Mask	£6
Niagara Falls Barrel	£5
Other Stunts	£10

Markets

Animal Markets	£15
Street Markets	£15

See note on pricing at beginning of section.

London Markets

Club Row	£8
Farringdon Road	£5
Petticoat Lane	£5
Billingsgate Market	£8
Smithfield Market	£8
Woolwich	£5

Travelling Fairs

Barnet Horse Fair	£20
Cosham Fair	£25
Hampstead Heath/A&G Taylor	£60
/Star Series	£5
Hull Fair	£20

Barnet Fair. R/P £20

Mitcham Fair	£20
Nottingham Goose Fair	£10
Oxford Fair	£15
Other named locations	£25
Fairground Equipment	£20
RP studies/Published c.1950	£5

See note on pricing at beginning of section.
There are in circulation many privately produced, postcard-size plain back photographs of Fairground equipment.
Most of these have been printed in quantity from an existing negative and consequently have only a nominal value.

FIRE BRIGADE

Firemen	£12
Fire fighting/Identified	£12
/Unidentified	£6
Fire Stations	£18
Tuck Oilettes	£8

Fire Engines

Hand Drawn	£40
Horse Drawn	£40
Motor	£40

Fires

Bon Marche/Brixton	£5
Lewes	£6
Selby Abbey	£3
Other GB Fires	£12
Art Sketches	£3

London Salvage Corps R/P £40

FISHING INDUSTRY

Deep Sea Fishing

Fish sales on quayside	£15
Fish Markets	£3
General quayside scenes	£3
Herring Girls	
/Gutting/Packing Herring	£6
/Spectacular RP studies	£15
Fishermen	£3
Mending Nets	£3
Fishwives at Newhaven etc.	£1
French scenes/Concarneau etc.	£3
Other French scenes	£2
Foreign scenes	£1.50

It is pointed out that in the 'Fish Markets' classification there are a number of very common cards, worth about £1.50 each, which are always turning up.
Unfortunately it is not possible to list these individually without showing illustrations, but you have been warned.

Trawlers/Drifters

RP Trawler studies	£12

General studies	£6
/c.1960 RP studies	£1.50
On board Trawler	£12
Trawler fleet at sea	£3

Tuck Oilette Series

2317	Toilers of the Sea	£4
2761	Toilers of the Sea	£4
2817	Toilers of the Sea	£4
6690	Toilers of the Deep	£4

Local Industry

Keddle Net Fishing/Rye	£25
Prawn Fishermen/Bognor	£15
Coracle Fishermen	£5
Cockle Gatherers	£10
Cockle Vendors	£15

GIPSIES

Camps

GB locations	£35
/Unlocated	£12
Alien Immigrants/Pub. Hartmann	£6
Macedonian Gipsies at Epping	£10

On the Road

GB locations	£35
/Unlocated	£12

HUNTING

Tuck Oilette Series

2732	Fox and Stag Hunting	£4
2758	Hunting	£4
3596	Hunting in the Shires	£4
9801	In the Hunting Field	£4

Miscellaneous

Photographic groups/Named Hunts	£6
/Un-named Hunts	£3
Other photographic studies	£3
The Owl Series	£1.50
Comic Sketches	£2
Art Studies	£3

INDUSTRIAL

Delabole Slate Quarry	£5
Gas Works	£15
Greenwich Telescope	£2
Power Houses	£6
Printing Works	£6
/Evening News	£8
Royal Mint/Two sets of 12 cards	
Price per set	£1.50
Saltworks	£25
Science Museum Series	£3
Steelworks	£12

Cotton Mills

Interior/Machines	£8
Exterior views	£8
Lancashire Weaving scenes	£8

Factories

Interior/Machines	£8
Exterior views	£8
Machine Shops	£6
Men at work	£6
Cammell Laird/20 cards	
Industrial sketches	£6
Vickers of Barrow/Production scenes	
RP series/Valentine	£8
Woolwich Arsenal WHS Series	£6

Pottery Industry

Factory Scenes	£6
Exteriors/Kilns etc.	£12
Craft Pottery/Throwing etc.	£10
Poole Pottery/14 cards	£3
Worcester Royal Porcelain Co. Ltd/	
Set 6/Tuck Oilette	£1.50

Tin Mining/Cornish Mines

RP/Close-up view	£25
/Middle distance	£15
Printed views	£10
Refining/Dressing processes/RP	£40

The great majority of Tin Mining cards were produced as Real Photographs by local photographers such as Bragg, Govier and Caddy etc.

MEDICAL

Asylums	£5
Operations/Surgical	£8
Ward Scenes	£6
Cottage Hospitals	£5
Hospitals	£5
Nurses	£3
Red Cross	£5
St. John's Ambulance Brigade	£5

Ambulances

Horse-Drawn	£35
Motor	£25

Dentistry

Surgeries	£15
Comic Sketches	£12

St. John's Ambulance R/P £5

POLICE

Policemen/RP portraits	£6
Police Stations	£12
Special Constabulary/RP portraits	£5
Comic Sketches	£3
Art Studies	£4

POSTAL

Royal Mail Vans	£35
Hand Carts/Traps	£35
Pillar Boxes	£5
Romantic/Greetings	£3
Comic Telegrams	£3
Comic Sketches	£3

Mail Coaches

At named locations/G.B.	£25
Art Type	£5

POSTMEN

RP Studies	£12
Art Studies	£5
Comic Sketches	£4

Postmen of the World/Set 48

Kunzli Freres	£10

Postmen of the British Empire/Set 14

Colman's Starch	£10

POST OFFICES

Sorting Offices	£20

Villages £20

Towns

Main Office	£15
Sub Post Office	£25

Cities

Main Offices	£8
Sub Post Office	£25

See note on pricing at beginning of section.

Delivery Vehicles/Staff Groups

Posed outside building	£50

RELIGION

ANGLICAN CHURCH

Bishops	£1.50
Clergy named	£1.50
Events/Processions	£5

Evangelism

Caravans	£25
Church Army	£3
Conventions/Meetings	£6
Gipsy Smith	£3
Personalities	£3
Wesleyan Churches	£3

Oberammergau

Actors/Portraits	£1
Production scenes/Views	£1

ROMAN CATHOLICISM

Cardinals/Bishops	£1.50
Priests named	£1.50
Events/Processions etc.	£2
Lourdes scenes	£1

Popes

Coronation Souvenir Cards	£5
Jubilee Cards	£5
Mourning Cards/Leo XIII	£5
Funeral Processions	£3
Portraits	£2

MISCELLANEOUS

Angels/Saints etc.	£4
Lord's Prayer	£1.50
Mission Societies	£2
Missionaries	£3
/In the Pot	£3
Monks/Local Industry	£2

For Churches and Religious buildings see
TOPOGRAPHICAL

RETAIL TRADE
Delivery Vehicles

Hand Carts	£35
Horse-drawn Carts	£40
Milk Floats	£50
Motor Vehicles	£30

See also MOTOR TRANSPORT

Public Houses

Delivery Vehicles/Staff Groups posed outside building	£50
Close-up view	£25
Pub in street scene	£10

See note on pricing at beginning of section.
A pub in a street scene would be priced as a
Topographical card. It must also be borne in
mind that there are many very common pubs
to be found on postcards. For example:
The Star/Alfriston, Bull and Bush/Hampstead,
Cat and Fiddle/New Forest,
Jerusalem Inn/Nottingham and many others
too numerous to list. These are worth much
less than the quoted prices and only through
experience will you learn which ones they are.

Breweries

Guinness Brewery Scenes	£8
6x4 size	£6
Local Breweries	£30

Shop Front, Super name 'Dross'! R/P £35

Shop Fronts

Delivery Vehicles/Staff Groups posed outside building	£50
Special Displays/Meat Hanging etc.	£40
Grocer/Tobacconist/Newsagent etc.	
Spectacular Close-up RP/Located	£35
/Unlocated	£15
Other displays/Located	£15
/Unlocated	£5
Picture Postcard Displays	£50
Arcades	£10
Rationing queues	£40
Station Bookstalls/W.H.S. etc.	£20

See note on pricing at beginning of section.
There are far more unlocated Shop Fronts
than those which can clearly be assigned to a
particular town or village.

RURAL LIFE

Allendale Wolf	£5
Barrel Organs/Men	£60
Blacksmiths	£18
Bootmakers	£25
Brusher Mills	£5
Children's Games	£5
Chimney Sweeps	£25
Cliff Climbers	£8
Coopers	£18
Cornish Pasties	£2
Deer Stalking	£3
Flower Shows	£8
Hermits	£12
Hunting/Shooting	£3
Milkmaids	£3
Odd Characters	£12
Open Air Gatherings	£5
Ox Roasts/Pig Roasts	£25
Pea Picking	£5
Peat Digging	£6
Seaweed Gathering/Wracking	£3
Spinning/Weaving	£4
Irish Spinning Wheels	£1.50

Blacksmith R/P £18

Street Furniture/Troughs	£6
Street Parades/Processions	£15

Price is governed by the subject and location.

Tobacco Auctions/USA	£6
Trug Making	£40
Village Crafts	£3
Village Folk	£2
Village Life	£3

There are a number of Tuck Oilette series on this theme, which would carry the price of the respective Artist.

Water Carts	£30
Watercress Growing	£20
Wheelwrights	£30
Workers in the fields	£5

Charcoal Burning

Actual work in progress/RP	£25
Huts/Forest clearings etc.	£5

Folklore

Banbury Cross	£1.50
County Humour/Dialect	£1.50
Customs & Traditions	£1.50
Dunmow Flitch	£8
Ducking Stools/Stocks	£1.50
Epitaphs	£1.50
Ghosts	£2
Gretna Green	£1
Lady Godiva	£5

There are many cards of different personalities playing this part.

Legends	£1.50
Maypole Celebrations/Located	£18
/Unlocated	£5
Morris Dancers	£15
Well Dressing	£6
Witches	£5

Funerals

Celebrities	£18

Special Events/Processions	£12
Other Funerals	£6

Lacemaking

GB locations/Named Lacemakers	£25
Industrial/Factory scenes	£6
Belgium	£4
France	£8
Other Foreign	£5

Performing Bears

GB locations	£100
/Unlocated	£30
Foreign	£12

Refuse Collection

Dustcarts	£40

SCHOOLS

Universities/Colleges	£2
Public Schools/Eton etc.	£2
Grammar/Secondary	£6
Village Schools	£8
Classroom groups/Identified	£8
/Unidentified	£1.50

SEASIDE

Donkeys	£3
Bathing Machines	£5
Pierrot/Beach Shows	£5
Piers	£3
Punch & Judy	£12
Sand Models	£3
Seaside Amusements	£6

Beach Scenes

Animated RP	£10
General scenes	£1.50

HOLIDAY CAMPS

Butlins

Pre-1960	£4/£8
1961 onwards	£2

Butlins produced cards with inset pix of their respective Holiday Camps.

Harrogate Pierrot's R/P £5

Pontins/Warners etc.

Pre 1960	£3
1961 onwards	£1.50

Local Camps/Holiday Villages

Pre 1960	£3/
1961 onwards	£1.50
Caravan Parks	£3

There exist many modern 6x4 size cards of Holiday Camps which would be worth less than the prices quoted above.

Tickeridge Mill R/P £18

WATERMILLS

Scarce types	£18
Middle range	£5
Common types	£2
Fires/Disasters	£25
Art types	£1
Foreign	£1.50

WINDMILLS

Scarce types	£35
Middle range	£15
Common types	£3
Fires/Disasters	£35

Thorpeness Windmill R/P £12

Art types	£1.50
Foreign	£3

See note on pricing at beginning of section.
With both Watermills and Windmills it is difficult to be more specific, without listing and illustrating every card. In both cases there are some very common cards which are always turning up. With Watermills, those at Laxey, Groudle Glen and Guy's Cliff are familiar to all collectors,while in Windmills, Salvington, Rottingdean and Wimbledon are virtually unsaleable. Beyond these, there is a broad band of middle range cards, which although relatively common, are usually saleable if priced realistically. At the top of the range are cards which are seldom found, and where only a few copies may exist.
Also with Windmills there are many post-1945 cards which would carry half the prices.quoted above.
Only knowledge and experience can be your guide.

WELFARE ORGANISATIONS

Workhouses	£12
N.S.P.C.C.	£12
Y.M.C.A./Y.W.C.A.	£3
John Grooms's Crippleage	£1.50
Lord Mayor Treloar Home	£1.50
Newcastle-upon-Tyne Street Life/	
Pub. Thompson & Lee	£15
Waifs and Strays	£3
Childrens' Homes	£6
Orphanages	£5

Charities/Fund Raising

Flag Days	£15
Fund Raising Animals	£12
T.B. Fund Raising	£8

See also MILITARY/WW1

Dr. Barnado at his desk Pr. £3

Dr. Barnardo

Portraits	£3
Funeral Procession at Barkingside	£20
Homes	£3
Children at Work	£3
Children in group photos	£3
'Our Young Migrants in Canada'	£12

This was a scheme now discredited where Barnardos sent children to the Colonies. Believed to be two sets of 6 cards.

Salvation Army Band. R/P £6

Salvation Army

Bands	£6
Gen. Booth/Visits G.B.	£20
Gen. Booth/Memorial Card	£8
Gen. Booth/Portraits	£3/£12
Miscellaneous interest	£3

YOUTH ORGANISATIONS
SCOUTING
Baden Powell

Tuck Empire Series	£25
Early Vignettes/Coloured	£25
/b.w.	£12
Relief of Mafeking	£30
Portraits	£12
Visits	£20

Portraits/Groups

Tuck R. & Sons/Payne H	£25
Other Series	£10
Camps/Located	£10
/Unlocated	£5
Scouts/Troops Identified	£10
/Unidentified	£2
Comic Sketches	£10

National Series
Published by Millar & Lang in sets of 6 cards.

Prices are for individual cards.

Series 749	£10
Series 760	£10

Series 845	£10
Series 858	£10
Series 919	£10
Series 1000	£10
Series 1002	£10
Series 1044	£10
Series 1572	£10
Price per set of those listed above	£75
Other Millar & Lang issues	£8

Personalities

Jack Cornwell V.C.	£10

Miscellaneous

H.Q. Official Cards	£15
Jamborees	£15

A special postmark on these cards adds to their value.

Tuck R. & Sons/Our Boy Scouts/ Oilette Series 9950/Animal Heads W.H. Ellam	£100
Price per set	£750
Scouts of the World/Set 111 USA 1968/Price for complete set	£75

GIRL GUIDES
Leaders

Lady Baden Powell	£10
Princess Mary	£5
Princess Elizabeth	£5
Other Leaders	£5

Portraits/Groups

Official Cards	£5
Identified	£5
Unidentified	£1.50

MISCELLANEOUS

Boys Brigade	£10
Church Lads Brigade	£6
Other Organisations	£3

Lady Baden Powell R/P £10

LONDON LIFE
and other Social History Series

Many Edwardian postcard firms published series of cards reflecting the Life and Labour of those times, while other companies produced long series covering Events and Disasters. These cards today are highly prized, and in many cases form a unique historical record of social conditions. The value of the Picture Postcard as a contemporary reference can be clearly seen in many of the examples listed below.

Market Report
Very little movement in this market. Popular among some established dealers who have advanced collections and have given up looking for the gaps.

ARISTOPHOT

391 Flower Girls	£10
392 Omnibus	£25
395 Policeman	£10
398 Omnibuses in a row	£15
401 Feeding Pigeons	£15
413 Street Vendors	£12
414 Hansom Cab	£20
415 Sandwich Types	£10
417 Boot Cleaner	£12
418 Fine Ripe Cherries	£10
419 London Beer	£20

BEAGLES J. & CO.

001 The Costermonger	£18
002 The Policeman	£18
003 The Shoe Black	£12
004 The German Band	£12
005 The Parcel Post	£20
006 The Flower Sellers	£10
006 The Horse Omnibus	£18
007 A Newsvendor	£12
008 The Flower Sellers	£10
008 The Street Organ	£15
010 The Knife Grinder	£15
011 Drinking Fountain & Cattle Trough	£10
013 The Pavement Artist	£12
014 The Paper Boy	£12
015 The Telegraph Messenger	£12
018 The Milkman	£18
018 The Flower Sellers	£10
019 The Baker	£15
020 The Postman	£15
022 The Chelsea Pensioner	£10
411 Dust Cart	£20
646K A London Policeman	£12
647N Policeman holding up the traffic	£12
648E City of London Ambulance	£18

W. HAGELBERG
Series 3490

Thames Embankment	£8
Coffee & Cocoa Stall	£8
Middlesex Street/Old Petticoat Lane	£8

JOHN WALKER

22607 Street Music	£25
22671 Petticoat Lane	£15
22672 Petticoat Lane	£15
22691 Bank Holiday	£30

LL/LOUIS LEVY
London Types

301 Beefeater at the Tower of London	£8
302 Pavement Artist	£8
303 The Fireman	£12
325 Policeman	£8

G. SMITH
Types of London Life

01 Pavement Artist	£8
04 Flower Seller at Piccadilly Circus	£12
05 Newsboy	£12
05a A Newsboy	£12
06 Shoe Black at Trafalgar Square	£12
07	
08 The Fireman	£12
09 A Bus Driver	£15
10 Police Ambulance	£15
11 Policeman holding up Traffic at the Bank	£12
12 Postman	£12
13 Messenger Boy	£12
14 Street Sweeper	£15
15 Fruit Seller	£15
16 Hot Chestnut Man	£15
17 The Lord Mayor's Coachman	£12
18 Punch & Judy Show at National Portrait Gallery	£15
19 A Horse Bus	£15
20 A Messenger Boy	£12
21	
22 Sentry at Buckingham Palace	£8

Research by Philip Richards who informs me that although this is the main series of Gordon Smith "Types of London Life", there are certain titles known in another un-numbered series, as well as other cards in the style within the publisher's general range.

PHOTOCROM CO.
Celesque Series/Coloured
London Types

Covent Garden Porter	£6
Shoe Black	£10
Flower Seller	£6
The Smithfield Market Porter	£6
The Bus Conductor	£10
The Pavement Artist	£6
The Recruiting Sergeant	£6
The Street Hawker	£10
The Newsboy	£6
The Life Guard	£6
The Orderly Boy	£10
The Postman	£10
The Chelsea Pensioner	£6
The Lighterman	£10

CHARLES SKILTON

Set of 12 cards c.1940	£18

TUCK R. & SONS

A10 A Policeman	£12
A11 The Recruiting Sergeant	£12
A12 A Fruit Hawker	£18
A13 Flower Vendors	£12
A14 A Messenger Boy	£12
A15 A Shoeblack	£18
A16 A Pavement Newsvendor	£12
A17 A Sandwichman & Newsvendor	£18
A18 A Cabman on the Rank	£18
A19 A Policeman controlling Traffic	£12
A20 A Pavement Hawker	£18
A21 A Pavement Artist	£12

WYNDHAM SERIES

6335 Hawking Butcher	£30
7579 Fish Stall	£30
7587 Mending Door Mats	£30
7588 Penny Scales	£30
7589 Salt & General Merchant	£30
7590 Sweep snow away	£30
7591 The Potman	£30
7592 Shrimps	£30
7593 Mixed Quartette	£30
7594 Caravan Carpenter	£30
7595 Hot Potatoes	£30
7596 Fruit Merchant	£30
7597 Pussy's Butcher	£30
7598 Sweeps	£30
7599 Muffins	£30
7600 Toy Vendor	£30
7601 Old Clo	£30
7602 Dustman	£30
7603 Shoeblack	£30
7604 Shoeblack	£30
7605 Street Musician	£30
7606 Whelks	£30
7607 Laces	£30

STAR SERIES
Set of 36 cards

01 Good Old Hampstead. The Cockney's Paradise
02 Milk Fresh from Tin Cow at St. James' Park.
03 The Nurse's Paradise, Hyde Park.
04 Feeding the Ducks in a London Park
05 Feeding the Pigeons in a London Park
06 The Fountains. Trafalgar Square.
07 Sweep O.
08 O.H.M.S.
09 The Little Bird will tell your Fortune for one Penny
10 Shoeblack and Cabby.
11 Fireman and Escape.
12 On Guard. Buckingham Palace.
13 Recruiting Sergeant and a Policeman. "On Point Duty".
14 Aliens.
15 Harmony.
16 A free Drink for Man's Best Friend.
17 Fine Fruit and Fresh Flowers. Farringdon Market, Farringdon Street.
18 Covent Garden.
19 All a Blowing and a Growing.
20 A Hot Day. Give us a Taster Jack.
21 Kerbstone Merchants. "Wonderful Pennorths". Ludgate Hill.
22 Paper Kiosk outside the "Prudential" Holborn. A well-known Landmark.
23 Regent Circus. "Fresh from Market".
24 The Busy Bargees. River Thames.
25 Off to a Fire.
26 Changing the guard. Horseguards.
27 Fatigue Duty. Buckingham Palace Road.
28 Motor Bus.
29 Electric Tram and "2d" Tube Station.
30 A Free Drink in a London Park.
31 London Bridge
32 Piccadilly Circus
33 Rotten Row. Hyde Park.
34 Mansion House and Cheapside.
35 G.P.O. and St. Martin's le Grand.
36 Holborn Viaduct and City Temple.

Price Range: £3/£6. (The printing technique of this series leaves much to be desired).

A & G TAYLOR
Orthochrome Series/Coloured

243 Taking Lessons from the Artist	£6
245 Cat's Meat!	£10
246 The Ice Cream Merchant	£10
247 The Crossing Sweeper	£10
248 Brother Professionals	£6
250 On His Majesty's Service	£10
251 "Here you are, Sir! Shine Sir?"	£10
254 London Postman making collection	£10

ROTARY PHOTOGRAPHIC CO.
London Life/Series 10513

01 Fireman	£25
02 Postman	£25
03 Street Orderly Boy	£25
04 Taxi-Cab Driver	£25
05 Newspaper Boy	£25
06 Pavement Artist	£20
07 Hot Chestnut Seller	£35
08 Lifeguardsman Sentry	£20
09 Toy Seller	£25
10 "Votes for Women"	£65
11 District Messenger	£25
12 Flower Seller	£25
13 Omnibus Driver	£35
14 Hansom "Cabby"	£35
15 Bootblack	£30
16 Hawker	£25
17 City Police Constable	£25
18 Flower Sellers	£20
19 Fortune Teller	£25
20 The Brewers Man	£35
21 District Messenger Boy	£25
22 Big Bens Telescopeman	£25
23 Post Office Telegraph Boy	£30
24 LCC Tramcar Conductor	£35
25 Reuter Telegraph Co.'s Messenger	£20
26 The Milkman	£35
27 The Baked Potato Man	£35
28 A Woman Pavement Artist	£25
29 City Police Motor Ambulance	£30
30 "Votes for Women"	£65
31 Billingsgate Porter	£25
32 Smithfield Market Porter	£35
33 Covent Garden Porters	£35
34 Chelsea Pensioner	£25
35 Firemen at Work	£20
36 Street Fruit Hawker/ Coster Barrow	£35
37 Street Orderly Man	£35
38 Boy Scouts	£35
39 Chimney Sweep	£25
40 Sandwich Board Man	£35
41 Automatic Road Sweeper	£35
42 Royal Exchange Constable	£25
43 Newspaper Boys with latest news	£30
44 Ice Cream	£35
45 An Apple Woman	£25
46 Recruiting Sergeants	£20
47 Coster in his Donkey Cart at Covent Garden Market	£35
48 Flower Sellers at Oxford Circus	£35
49 Underground Tube Train Conductor	£45
50 Boulters Lock on Ascot Sunday	£35
51 A Scene at Henley during Regatta Week	£35
52 A Racecourse Scene at Epsom	£35
53 The King is Coming	£35
54 Opera enthusiasts. Queue outside Covent Garden Opera House	£35
55 A Night Watchman	£35
56 A Coffee Stall Supper, "Al Fresco"	£35
57 A Whelk Stall	£35
58 A Motor Bus. One of London's Red Generals	£45
60 Postman collecting the Midnight Post	£35
60 Fireman at work at a midnight Fire	£30
61 An Underground Railway Lift Man	£35
62 GPO Royal Mail Motor	£35
63 Knives and Scissors Grinder	£35
64 A Baker's Man	£35
65 A Flower Seller	£35
66 A Coal Man	£40
67 A Butcher	£35
68 A Hospital Nurse	£45
69 Early Morning in Rotten Row, Hyde Park	£25
70 Football. Chelsea V Aston Villa at Stamford Bridge	£130
71 Arrest of a Militant Suffragette	£75
72 Rushing to a Fire at Night	£30
73 Steam Roller at work	£35
74 The Dustman	£35
75 A helpful member of our Dumb Friends League	£35
76 A Boy Scout's Band	£45
77 "Four Wheeler" Cab	£45
78 A City Window Cleaner	£35
79 Turkish Baths Advertiser	£35
80 A Labour Demonstration	£45
81 A Crossing Sweeper	£35
82 In Smithfield Meat Market	£35
83 Lifeguard at Whitehall	£35
85 "The policeman's lot is not a happy one"	£25
87 Feeding pigeons outside St. Paul's Cathedral	£20
88 In Billingsgate Market	£35
89 The Opening of the London Season	£35
90 Queen Alexandra Buying Roses	£20
91 A Coaching Meet in Hyde Park	£20
95 Fire Brigade drilling before Chief Officers	£45
96 Firemen wearing the smoke helmet	£45
98 Motor Fire Engine and Escape	£45
99 Fire Brigade drill at Headquarters	£45

There are also Tinted Cards known with a 10514 Series Number. More information is needed here.

LONDON LIFE/ART SERIES

Kyd	£10
Rotophot	
Cries of London	£3
Sauber	£5
Tuck R. & Sons	
Oilette Series 9015	£6

LYNMOUTH FLOODS

Francis Frith & Co., Reigate

LYH 29 "Back of Lyndale Hotel", horiz. R.P. £6

LYH 30 "Watersmeet Valley", horiz. R.P. £6

? LYH 31

? LYH 32

LYH 33 "Glen Lyn", horiz. R.P. £6

LYH 34 "The Main Street", horiz. R.P. £8

LYH 35 "East Lyn", horiz. R.P. £4

LYH 36 "Lynton Hill Corner", horiz. R.P. £12

? LYN 37 – LYH 40

LYH41 "Lyndale Hotel from Lynton Hill", horiz. R.P. £8

LYH 42 "View from the Quay", horiz. R.P. £6

? LYH 43

LYH 44 "Harbour and Quay from Lynton Hill", horiz. R.P. £6

All the above are thought to have been published also as printed cards. Value 50% of R.P. prices.

LYH 139 "Old Lynmouth / New Lynmouth", vert. RP £6

Harvey Barton & Son, Bristol

41850 (Lyndale Hotel and temporary foot-bridge), horiz. R.P. £15

41851 (Lyndale Hotel entrance), horiz. R.P. £8

41852 (Houses at bottom of Lynton Hill), horiz. R.P. £15

41853 (West Lyn Hotel and Lyn Valley Hotel), horiz. R.P. £15

The above 4 RP cards were also published without the border and given the serial numbers 1 – 4.

Unnumbered multi-view of above 4 views with central pre-flood view in oval, horiz. R.P £6

41854 "August 15th 1952 / Lynmouth / August 16th 1952", then and now comparison of West Lyn Hotel and Lyn Valley Hotel, vert R.P. £12

46268 "Lynmouth 1952 / Lynmouth 1953", then and now comparison of harbour, vert. R.P. £6

46269 "Lynmouth 1952 / Lynmouth 1953" R.P., then and now comparison looking seawards, vert. R.P. £6

Photochrom Co. Ltd., Tunbridge Wells

"Lynmouth after the Floods, August, 1952, The Electric Power Station and Flood", horiz. R.P. £8

"Lynmouth after the Floods, August, 1952 , The Cottage Tea Gardens and Café, River Side", horiz. R.P. £10

"Lynmouth after the Floods, August, 1952 , Lynn Valley Hotel", vert. R.P. £15

"Lynmouth after the Floods, August, 1952, Site of Shelley's Cottage", horiz. R.P. £18

"Lynmouth after the Floods, August, 1952, Lynn Valley Hotel", vert. R.P. £15

"Lynmouth after the Floods, August, 1952, Site of Eight Cottages washed away",horiz. R.P. £12

E.A.Sweetman & Son, Tunbridge Wells

C10412 "Old Lynmouth / New Lynmouth", then and now comparison, looking inland, vert. R.P. £6

? C10413

C10414 "Old Lynmouth / New Lynmouth", then and now comparison, looking seawards, vert. R.P. £6

? C10415

? C10416

C10417 "Old Lynmouth / New Lynmouth", then and now comparison, looking seawards from the new bridge, vert. R.P. £6

Anonymous

"Lynmouth Floods August 15th 1952", 5 different horiz. views, with letters N or M in the stamp box R.P. £10-15

Blackmore Series

"Lynmouth Disaster Aug. 15-16 1952", R.P., with footbridge in foreground and Lyndale Hotel entrance on left, horiz. R.P. £15

- Ditto, same title, looking seawards, with debris in foreground and bulldozer in middle distance, horiz. R.P. £15

- Ditto, same title, looking inland, with ruined building in right foreground, horiz. R.P £15

Information supplied by Colin Such, Warwick & Warwick Ltd

Canada, Fort Erie, Ontario.

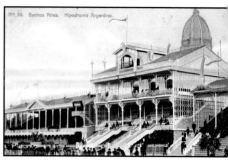
Argentina, Hippodrome, Beunos Aires

Cuba, Oriental Park Races, Havana

Brazil, The Jockey Club, Rio De Janeiro

Mexico, Agua Caliente

Chile, Tribunas del Club Hipico, Santiago

USA, Latonia, Kentucky

Peru, The Hippodrome, Lima

188

OVERSEAS RACECOURSES

Australia, Boulder City

New Zealand, Ellerslie, R/P

China, Shanghai

Singapore, Grand Stand

India, Grand Stand, Poona

South Africa, Pretoria

Japan, Yokohama

Southern Rhodesia, Salisbury

World Wide Racecourses price range between £4 & £7

OVERSEAS TOPOGRAPHICAL

Please read the following explanation before consulting prices:

1. Every country listed in this section could support its own catalogue. Many of them produced literally millions of postcards, and although I have now begun to sub-classify many countries, a process which will be continued in future editions of this Catalogue, it must be clearly understood that at best, all one can really do in the pages which follow, is to put the reader in touch with the broad general price area for any particular card.

2. The degree of classification of any one country is a reflection of the demand for that country. France catalogues in much greater depth than Luxembourg for example, because the demand is there. Readers may like to think about this, when choosing a country to collect? With many countries there exist definite market indications which allow me to list Town and City Street Scenes, while other `non-collected' countries can at present only be covered either with a general `Street Scene' heading, or, in many cases, with just a single price for the whole country!

3. To achieve a logical presentation, I have in all cases used the term `Street Scenes', but where applicable, e.g in small islands, this is taken to mean all population centres, hut settlements, native villages, dirt-track roads etc. I don't need to be told that there are few `Streets' in Tibet or Nepal - I have deliberately chosen to use this term throughout the listings to achieve a correct balance.

4. Railway Stations are in all cases taken to be Town or Village stations. It is suggested that main City stations or termini be treated as `General Views', unless of course you are faced with a quite spectacular card. With all Foreign cards you will find a great many which are virtually worthless. These include Beach Scenes • Cathedrals • Churches • Countryside • Gardens • Historic Buildings • Lake Scenes • Landscapes • Mountains • Parks • Religious Buildings • River Scenes • Ruins • Stately Homes • Waterfalls • WW1 Shell Damage • Volcanoes etc.

5. As far as possible within the confines of a logical presentation, I have listed countries under the name by which they were known at the turn of the century. Where applicable, I have also given the modern name of the country in brackets, followed by the date this name was adopted. (This is not necessarily the date of independence).

Prices...

... are given for both **Unused** and **Used** cards. With **Unused,** prices may be taken as a broad, general average for the classification to which they refer. However, in all classifications there will be some very common cards which are worth much less than the stated figure, whilst on the other hand there will be cards which are worth more. With **Used** cards, prices are for Postcards which are of non philatelic origin, bearing the correct postal rate for the period and distance involved, and with a clear cancel on the address side only. **The price given represents a basic value for any correctly used Postcard of that country.**

It is pointed out that some postally used cards from certain countries or Islands are particularly rare, and may fetch a price considerably in excess of that quoted. In these cases, and where these conditions also apply to unused cards, a + sign has been entered.

The + sign has also been used where a realistic market value has not yet been established. This does not necessarily mean that the Postcard in used form is particularly rare, although certainly worth the price quoted. At best, all one can do within the limitations of a Catalogue of this kind, is to offer the reader a general indication of value for the cards in which he is interested.

Market Report

The strength of the euro has made our prices look cheap to the many foreign dealers who now visit the UK. Consequently there is high demand for most European locations. In France and Germany 10 euros (currently £8) is more or less a starting price for anything collectible in dealers stocks. Italy, Russia, the Baltic States, Turkey, Romania are all strongly in demand followed by China, Australia and the Gulf states if you can find them.

	Unused	Used
ADEN		
South Yemen 1967		£6
Street Scenes	£2	
General Views	£1.50	
AFGHANISTAN		£12+
Ethnic	£3	
Street Scenes	£10	
General Views	£4	
ALBANIA		£3+
Ethnic	£3	
Street Scenes	£4	
General Views	£2	
ALGERIA		£1
Street Scenes	£2	
Ethnic	£2	
General Views	£1	
ANDAMAN ISLANDS		£15
General Views	£5	
ANDORRA		£5+
Street Scenes	£6	
General Views	£2	
ANGOLA		£5
Street Scenes	£6	
General Views	£2	
ANGUILLA		£20+
Street Scenes	£12	
General Views	£8	
ANTIGUA		£8+
Street Scenes	£10	
General Views	£2	
ARGENTINA	£2	
Ethnic	£3	
Railways	£6	
Street Scenes/Town	£3	
/City	£1.50	
/Rural	£4	
General Views	£1	
ASCENSION		£25+
Royal Visit	£25	£100+
General Views	£15	
AUSTRALIA		£1
Aborigines	£8	
Bush Life	£3	
Dairy Industry	£3	
Farming	£3	

Australia, Benalla Railway Station, £12

	Unused	Used
Industrial	£8	
Mining	£6	
Railway Stations	£12+	
Sheep Farming	£1.50	
Street Markets	£6	
Timber Industry	£4	
Trades/Workers	£4	
USA Fleet Visit	£18	
Street Scenes/Town	£6	
/City	£2	
/Rural	£8	
General Views	£1	
AUSTRIA		£1
Costume	£1.50	
Industrial	£3	
Railway Stations	£8	
Street Markets	£5	
Gruss Aus	£5	
Street Scenes/Town	£3	
/City	.50	
/Rural	£5	
General Views	.50	
AZORES		£3
Street Scenes	£5	
General Views	£2	
BAHAMAS		£4
Hurricane 1933	£10	
Ethnic	£3	
Street Scenes/Town	£6	
/Rural	£8	
USA coloured views	£2	
General Views	£2	

	Unused	Used
BAHRAIN		£20+
Street Scenes	£8	
General Views	£4	
BARBADOS		£5
Railway	£12	
Ethnic	£3	
Street Scenes	£5	
General Views	£1.50	

Barbados, Printed £5

	Unused	Used
BASUTOLAND		
Lesotho 1966		£15+
Ethnic	£2	
Street Scenes/Town	£8	
/Rural	£12+	
General Views	£3	
BECHUANALAND		
Botswana 1966		£15+
Ethnic	£5	
Street Scenes	£10+	
General Views	£3	
BELGIAN CONGO		
Zaire 1971		£4
Street Scenes	£6	
General Views	£1.50	
BELGIUM		.50
Costume	£1	
Dog Carts	£3	

8. MANAGE — Passage à niveau, Faubourg du Nord

Belgium, Manage, Pr. £6

	Unused	Used
Industrial	£6+	
Railway Stations	£8+	
Street Markets	£4	
Steam Trams	£8+	
Trades/Workers	£3	
WW1 Shell Damage	£1	
Street Scenes/Towns	£4	
/City	.50	
General Views	.50	
BERMUDA		£6+
Ethnic	£3	
Street Scenes/Town	£6	
General Views	£2	
BHUTAN	£25+	
Ethnic	£4	
Street Scenes	£10+	
General Views	£10+	
BOLIVIA		£5+
Ethnic	£2	
Railways	£6	
Street Scenes/Town	£5	
/Rural	£6	
General Views	£2	
BORNEO		
		£15+
Street Scenes/Town	£12+	
/Rural	£15+	
Dutch	£6	
BOSNIA & HERZEGOVINA		
Yugoslavia 1929		£2
Street Scenes	£3	
General Views	£2	
BRAZIL		£3
Ethnic	£3	
Railways	£6+	
Street Scenes/Town	£5+	
Street Scenes/City	£2	
General Views	£1	
BRITISH GUIANA		
Guyana 1966		£8
Ethnic	£5	
Sugar Industry	£4	
Street Scenes/Town	£6	
/Rural	£8+	
General Views	£3	
BRITISH HONDURAS		
Belize 1973		£15+
Timber Industry	£8	
Street Scenes/Town	£10+	
/Rural	£15+	
General Views	£5	

Canal Zone, Canal Hotel, pr. £5

	Unused	Used
BRITISH NEW GUINEA		
Papua New Guinea 1975		£15+
Ethnic	£10+	
Street Scenes	£20	
General Views	£8+	
BRITISH SOMALILAND		
Somalia 1960		£8
Street Scenes	£15	
General Views	£6	
BRITISH VIRGIN ISLANDS		£12
Street Scenes	£15	
General Views	£6	
BRUNEI		£25+
Street Scenes	£12	
General Views	£8	
BULGARIA		£1
Ethnic	£3	
Street Scenes	£4	
General Views	£1	
BURMA		£8
Ethnic	£3	
Street Scenes	£4	
General Views	£2	
CAICOS ISLANDS		£15
Street Scenes	£15+	
General Views	£12	
CAMBODIA		£8+
Kampuchea 1979		
Temples	£1	
Street Scenes	£8+	
General Views	£2	
CAMEROON		£10
Street Scenes	£8	
General Views	£3	
CANADA		£1
Farming	£1	
Indians	£4	
Industrial	£5	
Lake Steamers	£3	
Mining	£3	
Railway/CPR Views	£3	
Railway Stations	£8	
Street Markets	£3	
Trades/Workers	£3	
Street Scenes/Town	£4	
/City	£2	
/Rural	£8+	
General Views	.50	
CANAL ZONE		£3
Ethnic	£3	
Panama Canal	£3	
Street Scenes	£8	
General Views	£1.50	

	Unused	Used
CANARY ISLANDS		£3
Ethnic	£2	
Street Scenes	£3	
General Views	£1.50	
CAPE VERDE ISLANDS		£3
General Views	£3	
CAROLINE ISLANDS		£20
Pelew Islands, Ethnic	£5	
CAYMAN ISLANDS		£15+
General Views	£10	
CEYLON		
Sri Lanka 1972		£1
Ethnic	£2	
Tea Plantations	£3	
Street Scenes/Town	£3	
/City	£2	
Temples	£1.50	
General Views	£1	
CHAD		£6
Street Scenes	£8+	
General Views	£1	
CHATHAM ISLAND		£10+
General Views	£8	
CHILE		£3
Ethnic	£2	
Railways	£10+	
Street Scenes/Town	£4+	
/City	£2	
General Views	£1	

Chile, Antofagasta, Pr. £4

	Unused	Used
CHINA		£6
Ethnic	£4	
Street Scenes/City	£5	
/Rural	£10+	
General Views	£3	
CHRISTMAS ISLAND		£25+
Atomic Tests	£10	
General Views	£18	
COCOS ISLANDS		£25+
General Views	£18	
COLOMBIA		£4
Ethnic	£3	
Railways	£10+	
Street Scenes	£5	
General Views	£2	
COMORO ISLANDS		£8+
General Views	£3	
COOK ISLANDS		£12+
Street Scenes	£10	
General Views	£8	
CORFU		£2
Street Scenes	£5	
General Views	£1	
COSTA RICA		£6+
Ethnic	£3	
Street Scenes	£8	
General Views	£2	
CRETE		£2
Ethnic	£5	
Street Scenes	£6	
General Views	£2	
CUBA		£2
Street Scenes	£4	
General Views	£1	

Cuba, Gran Paris Hotel, Pr. £4

	Unused	Used
CURACAO		
Netherlands Antilles		£5+
Street Scenes	£6	
General Views	£1	
CYPRUS		£8
Ethnic	£6	

	Unused	Used
Street Scenes	£10	
General Views	£4	
CZECHOSLOVAKIA		£1
Street Scenes	£3	
General Views	.75	
DAHOMEY		
Benin 1975		£6
Street Scenes	£8	
General Views	£3	

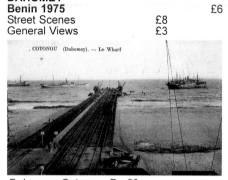

Dahomey, Cotonou, Pr. £3

	Unused	Used
DANISH WEST INDIES		
Virgin Islands/USA 1917		£15+
Ethnic	£5	
Street Scenes	£5	
General Views	£3	
DANZIG		
Poland 1945		£2
Street Scenes	£6	
General Views	£1.50	
DENMARK		£1
Costume	£1	
Street Scenes/Town	£3	
/City	£1	
General Views	£1	
DOMINICA		£6
General Views	£2	
DOMINICAN REPUBLIC		£2
General Views	£2	
DUTCH GUIANA		
Suriname 1975		£5
General Views	£3	
DUTCH NEW GUINEA		
Street Scenes	£6	
General Views	£3	
EASTER ISLAND		£25
General Views	£5	
ECUADOR		£4
Ethnic	£4	
Railways	£10+	
Street Scenes/Town	£6	
/City	£3	
General Views	£2	
EGYPT		£1
Ethnic	£2	
Street Scenes	£2	
General Views	£1	

	Unused	Used

ELLICE ISLANDS
Tuvalu 1978 £10+
Street Scenes £15
General Views £8

EL SALVADOR £4
Ethnic £3
Railway £10+
Street Scenes £5
General Views £2

ERITREA
Ethiopia 1952 £3
Ethnic £4
Street Scenes £8
General Views £1.50

ESTONIA
Russia 1940 £6
Ethnic £3
Street Scenes £8
General Views £1.50

Estonia, Parnu, R/P £8

ETHIOPIA £5+
Ethnic £3
Street Scenes £6
General Views £2

FALKLAND ISLANDS £20+
Events £25+
Penguins & Birds £8
Sheep Farming £12+
Whaling £15+
Street Scenes £20+
General Views £15+

FANNING ISLAND £15+
General Views £8+

FAROE ISLANDS £10+
General Views £6+

FIJI £5
Ethnic £6
StreetScenes £10+
General Views £3

FINLAND £4
Costume £1.50
Street Scenes/Town £5
/City £1.50
General Views £1

	Unused	Used

Fiji , Mountaneers House, Pr.   £3

FIUME
Yugoslavia 1947 £5
Street Scenes £6
General Views £1.50

FORMOSA
Taiwan £12+
Street Scenes £10+
General Views £3

FRENCH GUIANA £4
General Views £3

FRENCH GUINEA
Guinea 1958 £4
General Views £4

FRENCH INDIAN SETTLEMENTS
India 1950/54 £2
General Views £2

FRENCH OCEANIA £10+
Street Scenes £8+
General Views £4

FRENCH SOMALILAND
Djibouti 1977 £5
Street Scenes £8
General Views £1.50

FRENCH SOUDAN
Mali 1960 £3
Street Scenes £5
General Views £1.50

FRANCE .50
Animal Markets £6
Canals £1.50
Costume .50
Dog Carts £35+
Farming £3
Fetes £5
Fishing Industry £3
Street/Fish Markets £6
Industrial £5
Mining £5
Railway Stations £8
Synagogues £25
Trades/Workers £6
Watermills £3
Windmills £4
Street Scenes/Villages £6+
/Town £2+
/City £1
General Views .£1

France is arguably the leading postcard collecting country in the world, and its cards have been catalogued to a fine degree by Neudin and Fildier, whose annual publications are strongly recommended to those readers who wish to go more deeply into the subject.

	Unused	Used
GABON		£4
Street Scenes	£10	
General Views	£2	
GAMBIA		£8+
Street Scenes	£8	
General Views	£3	

Gambia, Bathurst, Pr. £3

GERMAN EAST AFRICA		£10+
Burundi 1962/Rwanda 1962/Tanzania 1961		
Ethnic	£5	
Occupation 1914/18	£6	
Street Scenes	£8	
General Views	£3	
GERMAN NEW GUINEA		
Papua New Guinea 1975		£20+
Ethnic	£8	
Street Scenes	£10	
General Views	£4	
GERMAN SOUTH WEST AFRICA		
Namibia		£8+
Ethnic	£8	
Street Scenes	£10	
General Views	£3	
GERMANY		£1
Animal Markets	£5	
Costume	£1.50	
Farming	£1.50	
Industrial	£5	
Mining	£4	
Railway Stations	£8	
Rhine Steamers	£3	

	Unused	Used
Street Markets	£5	
Synagogues	£25	
Trades/Workers	£5	
Street Scenes/Town	£3	
/City	£1	
General Views	.50	
GIBRALTAR		
Street Scenes	£2	
General Views	.50	
GILBERT ISLANDS		
Kiribati 1979		£20+
Street Scenes	£12	
General Views	£8	
GOLD COAST		
Ghana 1957		£6
Ethnic	£6	
Railway	£10	
Street Scenes	£8	
General Views	£2	
GREECE		£2
Ethnic	£3	
Postal Stationery	£8	
Street Scenes	£8	
General Views	£2	
GREENLAND		£20+
Ethnic	£6	
Street Scenes	£10	
General Views	£5	

Greenland, Julianehaab, R/P. £5

GRENADA		£5+
Street Scenes	£5	
General Views	£1.50	
GUADELOUPE		£3
Street Scenes	£8	
General Views	£1.50	
GUAM		£10+
Street Scenes	£8	
General Views	£4	

	Unused	Used
GUATEMALA		£4
Street Scenes	£6	
General Views	£2	
HAITI		£3
Street Scenes	£6	
General Views	£1.50	
HAWAII		£5
Ethnic	£4	
Street Scenes colour	£3	
Street Scenes photo	£10	
General Views	£1.50	

Hawaii, Honolulu, Pr.   £3

	Unused	Used
HELIGOLAND		£2
Street scenes	£6	
General Views	£2	
HONDURAS		£4
Ethnic	£4	
Railway	£10	
Street Scenes	£8	
General Views	£2	
HONG KONG		£6
Ethnic	£4	
Peak Railway	£5	
Street Scenes Photo	£12	
Street Scenes colour	£6	
General Views	£4	
HUNGARY		£2
Ethnic	£3	
Street Scenes	£4	
General Views	£1	
ICELAND		£10+
Ethnic	£5	
Street Scenes	£8	
General Views	£2	
INDIA		£1
British Rule/Barracks etc.	£2	
Ethnic	£2	
Holy Sites	£1	

Court Size	£8	
Street Scenes	£3	
General Views	£1.50	
IRAQ		£6
British Occupation	£4	
Street Scenes	£8	
General Views	£2	

Iraq, 'Shopfront' Pr.   £8

ITALY		.50
Costume	£1	
Industrial	£5	
Railway Stations	£10	
River Steamers	£3	
Street Markets	£6	
Trades/Workers	£3	
Street Scenes/Town	£3	
/City	.50	
IVORY COAST		£8
Street Scenes	£10	
General Views	£2	
JAMAICA		£3
Ethnic	£3	
Railway	£10	
Sugar Industry	£3	
Street Scenes	£5	
General Views	£1	
JAPAN		£2
Costume	£1	
Ethnic	£2	
Tea Houses	£2	
Yokohama Earthquake	£3	
Street Scenes/City	£3	
/Rural	£5	
General Views	£1	
JAVA		£3
Street Scenes	£5	
General Views	£3	
KENYA		£4
Ethnic	£6	
Street Scenes	£6	
General Views	£2	

	Unused	Used
KERMADEC ISLAND		£20+
General Views	£5	
KOREA		£8+
Street Scenes	£6	
General Views	£2	

Korea, Seoul, Pr. £6

	Unused	Used
KUWAIT		£20+
Street Scenes	£8	
General Views	£4	
LABUAN		£15+
Street Scenes	£12+	
General Views	£8	
LAOS		£10
Street Scenes	£10	
General Views	£3	
LATVIA		
Russia 1940		£4
Ethnic	£5	
Street Scenes	£5	
General Views	£2	
LEBANON		£5
Ethnic	£3	
Street Scenes	£4	
General Views	£1.50	
LIBERIA		£10+
Street Scenes	£8	
General Views	£2	
LIBYA		£2
General Views	£2	
LIECHTENSTEIN		£3
Street Scenes	£6	
General Views	£2	
LITHUANIA		
Russia 1940		£5
Ethnic	£4	
Street Scenes	£5	
General Views	£2	
LORD HOWE ISLAND		£20+
General Views	£12	

	Unused	Used
LUXEMBOURG		.50
Street Scenes	£2	
General Views	.50	
MACAO		£20
Street Scenes	£12	
General Views	£6	
MADAGASCAR		£3
Street Scenes	£6	
General Views	£1	

Madagascar, Diego Suarez Pr. £6

	Unused	Used
MADEIRA		£3
Street Scenes	£3	
General Views	£1	
MAFIA ISLAND		£25+
General Views	£6	
MALAYA		
Malaysia 1963		£5
Ethnic	£4	
Railways	£10	
Rubber Industry	£3	
Street Scenes	£6	
General Views	£1.50	
MALDIVE ISLANDS		£10+
General Views	£8	
MALTA		.50
Ethnic	£3	
Street Scenes/RP	£5	
/Coloured	.50	
General Views	.50	
MARTINIQUE		£3
Volcano 1902	£3	
Street Scenes	£8	
General Views	£1	
MAURITANIA		£3
Street Scenes	£8	
General Views	£2	
MAURITIUS		£6
Railways	£15	
Street Scenes	£8	
General Views	£3	

	Unused	Used
MEXICO		£2
Ethnic	£3	
Railways	£10	
Street Scenes	£4	
General Views	£1	

Mexico, Tijuana, Pr. £3

MIDDLE CONGO		
Congo 1960		£6
Street Scenes	£8	
General Views	£2	
MOLUCCA ISLANDS		
General Views	£5	
MONACO		.50
Street Scenes	£1	
General Views	.50	
MONGOLIA		£10+
General Views	£6	
Ethnic	£6	
MONTENEGRO		
Yugoslavia 1929		£5
Street Scenes	£8	
General Views	£1.50	
MONTSERRAT		£12
General Views	£8	
MOROCCO		£1
Street Scenes	£3	
General Views	£1	
Ethnic	£2	

Mozambique, Lourenco Marques Pr. £3

	Unused	Used
MOZAMBIQUE		£4
Street Scenes	£5	
General Views	£1	
MUSCAT & OMAN		
Oman 1970		£30+
Street Scenes	£8	
General Views	£6	
NAURU		£25+
General Views	£10	
NEPAL		£10+
Ethnic	£3	
General Views	£5	
NETHERLANDS		.50
Canals	£1	
Costume	.50	
Customs & Traditions	£1	
Industrial	£3	
Railway Stations	£5	
Street Markets	£3	
Trades/Workers	£3	
Windmills	£1.50	
Street Scenes/Village	£4	
/Town	£1	
/City	.50	
General Views	.50	
NEVIS		£10+
General Views	£8	
NEW CALEDONIA		£10+
Street Scenes	£8	
General Views	£3	
NEWFOUNDLAND		£5
Fishing Industry	£5	
Railway Stations	£12	
Street Scenes	£8	
General Views	£4	
NEW HEBRIDES		£15+
Vanuata 1980		
Street Scenes	£10+	
General Views	£5	
NEW ZEALAND		£1
Dairy Industry	£3	
Farming	£1.50	
Industrial	£5	
Maoris	£3	
Railway Stations	£10+	
Sheep Farming	£1	
Street Markets	£5	
Trades/Workers	£5	
Street Scenes/Town	£6	
/City	£3	
General Views	.75	
NICARAGUA		£6
Ethnic	£6	
Railways	£12+	

	Unused	Used
Street Scenes	£8+	
General Views	£3	
NICOBAR ISLAND		£10+
General Views	£5	
NIGER		£3
Ethnic	£8	
Street Scenes	£6	
General Views	£1.50	
NIGERIA		£2
Ethnic	£3	
Railways	£8	
Street Scenes	£5	
General Views	£3	
NIUE		£15+
General Views	£8	
NORFOLK ISLAND		£20+
General Views	£18	
Street Scenes	£20	
NORTH BORNEO		
Sabah 1964		£15+
Ethnic	£6	
Street Scenes	£12+	
General Views	£4	
NORTHERN RHODESIA		
Zambia 1964		£6
Ethnic	£4	
Railways	£15+	
Street Scenes	£8	
General Views	£1.50	
NORWAY		£1
Costume	£1	
Street Scenes/Town	£5	
/City	£3	
General Views	£1	

Norway, Oslo, R/P. £3

	Unused	Used
NYASALAND		
Malawi 1964		£4
Ethnic	£4	
Street Scenes	£6	
General Views	£3	

	Unused	Used
OCEAN ISLAND		£15+
General Views	£8	
OUBANGUI-CHARI		
Central African Republic 1960		£5
General Views	£3	
PALESTINE		
Israel 1948		£1
British Occupation	£6	
Ethnic	£2	
Religious Sites	.50	
Street Scenes	£6	
General Views	£1	
PANAMA	£4	£4
Ethnic	£3	
Railways	£10+	
Street Scenes	£5	
General Views	£1.50	

Panama, Avenida Central, R/P £5

	Unused	Used
PAPUA NEW GUINEA		£10
Street Scenes	£10	
General Views	£6	
PARAGUAY		£3
Ethnic	£4	
Railways	£12+	
Street Scenes	£8	
General Views	£2	
PEMBA ISLAND		£20+
Ethnic	£6	
General Views	£6	
PERIM ISLAND		£15+
General Views	£5	
PERSIA		
Iran 1935		£8
Street Scenes	£10	
General Views	£5	
PERU		£5
Ethnic	£5	
Railways	£10+	
Street Scenes	£6+	
General Views	£2	

Philippines, Fire Station, Manila, £8

	Unused	Used
PHILIPPINES		£3
Street Scenes	£8	
General Views	£2	
PHOENIX ISLAND		£10+
General Views	£5	
PITCAIRN ISLAND		£40+
Ethnic	£20	
General Views	£15	
POLAND		£2
Ethnic	£2	
Street Scenes	£4	
General Views	£1.50	

Poland Pr. £4

	Unused	Used
PORTUGAL		£1
Costume	£1.50	
Industrial	£3	
Railway Stations	£8	
Street Markets	£5	
Trades/Workers	£4	
Street Scenes/Town	£4	
/City	£1	
General Views	.50	
PORTUGUESE GUINEA		
Guinea-Bissau 1974		£5
Street Scenes	£8	
General Views	£1.50	

	Unused	Used
PORTUGUESE INDIA		
India 1961		£1.50
General Views	£1.50	
PORTUGUESE TIMOR		
East Timor		£5
Street Scenes	£8	
General Views	£2	
PUERTO RICO		£4
Street Scenes	£8	
General Views	£2	
REUNION		£5
Ethnic	£6	
Street Scenes	£8	
General Views	£3	
ROMANIA		£1
Ethnic	£3	
Street Scenes	£5	
General Views	£2	
RUSSIA		£2
Costume	£2	
Ethnic	£6	
Industrial	£6	
Railway Stations	£10	
Street Markets	£8	
Trades/Workers	£10	
Street Scenes/Town	£5	
/City	£2	
General Views	£2	
ST. CROIX		£5+
Street Scenes	£6	
General Views	£4	
ST. HELENA		£12+
Boer War	£20	
Street Scenes	£10	
General Views	£3	
ST. KITTS		£8+
Street Scenes	£10	
General Views	£3	
ST. LUCIA		£8+
Street Scenes	£8	
General Views	£2	
ST. MARTIN		£8+
Street Scenes	£8	
General Views	£3	
ST. PIERRE & MIQUELON		£10+
Street Scenes	£8	
General Views	£2	
ST. THOMAS & PRINCE ISLAND		£6+
Street Scenes	£6	
General Views	£2	
ST. VINCENT		£8+
Street Scenes	£8	
General Views	£3	

	Unused	Used
SAMOA		£12+
Ethnic	£6	
Street Scenes	£10	
General Views	£5	
OAN MARINO	£2	£2
Street Scenes	£4	
General Views	£2	
SARAWAK		£10+
Ethnic	£8	
Street Scenes	£10	
General Views	£6	
SARDINIA		£1.50
Street Scenes	£5	
General Views	£1	
SAUDI ARABIA		£15+
Street Scenes	£8	
General Views	£4	
SENEGAL		£3
Street Scenes	£5	
General Views	£1.50	
SERBIA		
Yugoslavia 1929		£3
Ethnic	£3	
Street Scenes	£5	
General Views	£1.50	
SEYCHELLES		£15+
Street Scenes	£12+	
General Views	£8	
SIAM		
Thailand		£8+
Street Scenes	£10+	
General Views	£3	
SIERRA LEONE		£5
Ethnic	£3	
Railways	£10+	
Street Scenes	£6	
General Views	£2	
SIKKIM		
India 1975		£20+
General Views	£3	
Ethnic	£3	
SINGAPORE		£5
Ethnic	£5	
Railway Stations	£15+	
Street Scenes	£8	
General Views	£4	
SOLOMON ISLANDS		£20+
Street Scenes	£10+	
General Views	£6	

	Unused	Used
SOMALILAND		
Somalia 1960		£20+
Street Scenes	£8	
General Views	£3	
SOUTH AFRICA		£1
Ethnic	£2	
Industrial	£4	
Mining	£4	
Railways	£8	
Railway Stations	£8	
Trekking	£1.50	
Street Scenes/Town	£4	
/City	£1	
General Views	£1	

South Africa, Hotel, Natal, Pr. £4

	Unused	Used
SOUTHERN RHODESIA		
Zimbabwe 1980		£5
City Street Scenes	£6	
City Buildings	£4	
Town Street scenes	£12+	
General Views	£1.50	
SPAIN		£1
Bullfighting	£2	
Costume	£1	
Industrial	£4	
Railway Stations	£6	
Street Markets	£4	

Spain, Guernica, Pr. £3

	Unused	Used
Trades/Workers	£3	
Street Scenes/Towns	£3	
/City	£2	
General Views	.50	

SPANISH GUINEA
Equatorial Guinea 1968

	Unused	Used
		£4
Street Scenes	£8	
General Views	£3	

SUDAN

	Unused	Used
		£4
Ethnic	£4	
Street Scenes	£8	
General Views	£2	

SUMATRA

	Unused	Used
		£3
Street Scenes	£6	
General Views	£1	

SWAZILAND

	Unused	Used
		£10+
Ethnic	£4	
Street Scenes	£8	
General Views	£4	

SWEDEN

	Unused	Used
		£1
Costume	.50	
Street Scenes/Town	£3	
/City	£1	
General Views	.50	

Sweden, Gefle, Pr. £3

SWITZERLAND

	Unused	Used
		.50
Costume	£1	
Customs & Traditions	£1	
Industrial	£3	
Lake Steamers	£2	
Mountain Railways	£2	
Railway Stations	£8	
Trades/Workers	£5	
Street Scenes/Town	£3	
/City	£1	
General Views	.50	

SYRIA

	Unused	Used
		£3
Street Scenes	£4	
General Views	£1.50	

TANGANYIKA
Tanzania 1961

	Unused	Used
		£6
Ethnic	£5	
Street Scenes	£8	
General Views	£1.50	

TASMANIA

	Unused	Used
		£3
Street Scenes	£6	
General Views	£1.50	

THURSDAY ISLAND

	Unused	Used
		£10+
General Views	£8	

TIBET

	Unused	Used
		£25+
Ethnic	£10	
General Views	£20	

TIMOR

	Unused	Used
		£15+
Street Scenes	£6	
General Views	£3	

TOBAGO

	Unused	Used
		£5+
Street Scenes	£6	
General Views	£3	

TOGO

	Unused	Used
		£6
Ethnic	£6	
Street Scenes	£5	
General Views	£4	

TONGA

	Unused	Used
		£15+
Ethnic	£12	
General Views	£8	

TRANSJORDAN
Jordan 1946

	Unused	Used
		£4
Street Scenes	£6	
General Views	£1.50	

TRINIDAD

	Unused	Used
		£2
Ethnic	£3	
Oil Industry	£4	
Street Scenes	£6	
General Views	£2	

Trinidad, Port of Spain, Pr. £6

	Unused	Used
TRISTAN DA CUNHA (PRE 1928)		£250+
General Views	£100+	
TUNISIA		£2+
Street Scenes	£3	
General Views	£1	
TURKEY		£4+
Ethnic	£4	
Street Scenes/town	£6	
Street Scenes/city	£2	
General Views	£1	
TURKS ISLANDS		£20+
Street Scenes	£12	
General Views	£12	
TUVA		
Russia 1944		£10+
Street Scenes	£8	
General Views	£4	
UGANDA		£5+
Ethnic	£4	
Street Scenes	£6	
General Views	£2	
UPPER VOLTA		
Burkina 1984		£5+
Street Scenes	£8	
General Views	£1.50	
URUGUAY		£3
Ethnic	£4	
Railways	£10	
Street Scenes/Town	£5	
/City	£3	
General Views	£1.50	
U.S.A.		£1
Cattle	.50	

	Unused	Used
Indians	£6	
Industrial	£3	
Mining	£5	
Railway Stations	£6	
Steamboats	£3	
Street Scenes/Town	£4	
/City	£1	
General Views	.50	
VENEZUELA		£4
Ethnic	£5	
Railways	£10	
Street Scenes	£5	
General Views	£1.50	
VIETNAM		£3
Ethnic	£6	
Street Scenes	£8	
General Views	£3	
WAKE ISLAND		
General Views	£6	
YEMEN		£5+
Street Scenes	£6	
General Views	£4	
YUGOSLAVIA		£2
Ethnic	£3	
Street Scenes	£5	
General Views	£1.50	
ZANZIBAR		£8
Ethnic	£8	
Street Scenes	£6	
General Views	£1.50	

USA, Coach Company, LA-Venice, Pr. £4

USA, Allentown PA, Pr. £4

STAMPS ON POSTCARDS

In response to many enquiries we receive about the value of Stamps found on Postcards, it must be pointed out that the picture postcard invariably carried the minimum postage rate, and these low-denomination Stamps are virtually worthless. Realistically, the only value in a used card would be if it has been stamped and posted from an 'unusual' country, or small island, or if it bears a cancellation of some interest.

INLAND POSTAGE RATES

1 October 1870 - 3 June 1918 - $\frac{1}{2}$d
3 June 1918 - 13 June 1921 - 1d
13 June 1921 - 24 May 1922 - $1\frac{1}{2}$d
24 May 1922 - 1 May 1940 - 1d

FIRST DAY OF ISSUE

QUEEN VICTORIA

$\frac{1}{2}$d Blue Green	17 April 1900	£500

KING EDWARD VII

$\frac{1}{2}$d Blue Green	1 January 1902	£40
1d Red	1 January 1902	£40
$\frac{1}{2}$d Yellow Green	26 November 1904	£35

KING GEORGE V

$\frac{1}{2}$d Green (three-quarter profile, hair dark)	22 June 1911	£30
1d Red (three-quarter profile, Lion unshaded)	22 June 1911	£40
$\frac{1}{2}$d Green (three-quarter profile, Hair light)	1 January 1912	£40
1d Red (three-quarter profile, Lion shaded)	1 January 1912	£45
*British Empire Exhibition 1924. (1d Red)	23 April 1924	£15
*British Empire Exhibition 1925. (1d Red)	9 May 1925	£30
U.P.U Congress 1929 ($\frac{1}{2}$d or 1d)	10 May 1929	£12
$\frac{1}{2}$d Green	19 November 1934	£5
1d Red	24 September 1934	£5
Silver Jubilee 1935. ($\frac{1}{2}$d or 1d)	7 May 1935	£6

* Postcards bearing Wembley Park 1924 or 1925 handstamp or slogan cancel on exhibition cards would justify a premium.

KING EDWARD VIII

$\frac{1}{2}$d Green	1 September 1936	£6
1d Red	14 September 1936	£12

KING GEORGE VI

$\frac{1}{2}$d Green	10 May 1937	£1
1d Red	10 May 1937	£1

POSTMARKS ON POSTCARDS

This is a vast and complex field, and part of the much wider area of Philately. There are thousands of different postal markings and stamps to be found on the backs of picture postcards, and indeed there is a similar number of specialised philatelic books devoted to all aspects of this subject.

In a postcard Catalogue of this kind, it is only possible to give a very rough indication of price for postmarks likely to be found on picture postcards. Readers requiring more specialised information or catalogues are referred to any good stamp dealer, or to one of the many books available on the subject.

IMPORTANT. Prices quoted are for complete, clear postmarks in every instance. Partial or indistinct strikes, generally have very little value.

CIRCULAR DATE STAMP

English type - 50p
The most common of all postmarks

Scottish type - 75p upwards

SINGLE RING

50p upwards

Small 'thimble' circular ring
£1 upwards

DUPLEX

£1 upwards
Certain obscure or limited types may be worth up to £10 each

206

SQUARED CIRCLES

Three different types £1 each
For lesser used types - £2 upwards to £40

MACHINE CANCELLATIONS

There are many varieties and different types
As examples shown £1 each

MACHINE CANCELLATIONS £1-£3

Two different examples of the E (Crown) R Type. Used in London (£5) Liverpool (£20)

CACHETS

50p
Handstamps applied other than by the
Official PO. Other common types are
'Summit of Snowdon', "Beachy Head'

METER MARKS

50p
Normally meant for business use

POSTAGE DUES

From £1 upwards
Surcharge marks for under-paid mail, many varieties

(i)

(ii)

(iii)

EXAMINATION MARKS

Post Office Examiner's marks applied to wrongly sorted mail. Usually stamped in black
but type (iii) sometimes found in violet. 75p - £2 each
N.B. There is a larger type as (iii) which was used for checking the bulk posting of
circulars, etc. Price 50p each

RUBBER DATE-STAMPS

often in blue or violet, used by smaller offices
£3 - £10 if superb coloured

ISLANDS

Circular Date Stamps
Examples shown, Gorey £3, Sandwich Shetland £5. Others such as Lundy Island £40,
St. Kilda £25. Chief offices of Jersey, Guernsey and I.O.M are common

---

SLOGANS

50p upwards
Mostly common, but there are exceptions amongst many hundreds of different types

SKELETONS

A temporary hand-stamp used for a limited period. Of varying sizes usually 27 - 39 mm in diameter. Price subject to wide fluctuation £3-£10 upwards

EXHIBITIONS

Edinburgh 1908
£6

Crystal Palace Code 3
(below date) £20

A complex field where price depends upon the particular exhibition and date
£1. - £50

TRAVELLING POST OFFICES

£5
Another type of railway postmark
Many different £1.50 - £30

SORTING CARRIAGES & TENDERS

£5
Railway postmarks - where many types
and varieties exist

RECEIVED FROM H M SHIP
£1.50
Naval security markings

DUMB CANCELS
£1.50
Naval security markings

ARMY CAMPS
Many different varieties £2 - £20

ARMY & FIELD POST OFFICES

P.B.2
1919 Archangel
£25

Field Post Office G
France 1915
£1 upwards

A popular specialist field - with wide price fluctuations

ROYAL HOUSEHOLDS

There are several different date-stamped as
example above.
All are scarce £12 upwards

SEA POST MARKS

£1.50 upwards
A common Maritime strike

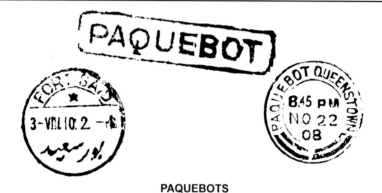

PAQUEBOTS

£2   £5

Typical examples of a very wide and complex field in maritime postal history

STEAMERS

£12 upwards
Used for mail carried by Paddle
Steamers. Other varieties could be
worth more.

RAILWAY SUB-OFFICES

75p+
R.S.O. postmarks. Certain types
are worth more

STAMPS ON POSTCARDS

Queen Victoria -1901

King Edward V111 - 1936

King Edward VII 1902-1910

King George VI 1937-1951

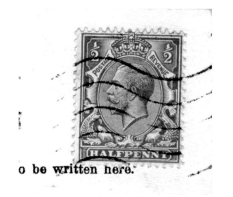

King George V - 1911-1935

Queen Elizabeth II - 1952-

CHRISTMAS POSTMARKS
For delivery on Christmas Day
1903 - 1909

Bury

(i)
£50 - £300

(ii)
£50 - £300

(iii)
£50

initials   City & Towns known to have used such cancellers

ADJ	Altrincham (i) (ii)		Newton Le Willows (ii)
	Ashton Under Lyne (ii)		Norwich (ii)
	Birkenhead (ii)		Oldham (ii)
BL	Bolton (i)		Ormskirk (ii)
BD	Bradford (i)		Prescot (ii)
BC	Bury (i)	PR	Preston (i)
CE	Carlisle (i)		Reading (ii)
	Douglas, I.O.M (ii)	RO	Rochdale (i)
DR	Dover (i)		Runcorn (ii)
	Dukinfield (ii)		St. Helens (ii)
ECC	Eccles (ii)	SCR	Sale (i)
GW	Glasgow (i)	SP	Southport (i)
	Glossop (ii)		Stalybridge (ii)
HU	Hull (i) (ii)	SP	Stockport (i) (ii)
	Hyde (ii)	WF	Wakefield (i)
KU	Knutsford (i) (ii)	SL	Walsall (i)
LE	Leicester (i) (ii)	WA	Warrington (i) (ii)
	Leigh (ii)	WIP	Widnes (i) (ii)
	Liverpool (ii)	WI	Wigan (i) (ii)
MC	Macclesfield (i)		
MR	Manchester (i) (ii) (iii)		

LA POSTE AUX INDES ANGLAISES

INDEX